"If you're as curious as I am, you've probably wondered about the possibility of alien life in the universe. Are there other planets suitable for life as we know it? Could aliens ever visit us, or have they visited us in the past? Would the existence of aliens mean that Christianity is untrue? There's no one better to ask than Jeff Zweerink. Jeff tackles the subject matter from the perspective of an astrophysicist and Christian believer, and he's written a book *everyone* can understand. *Is There Life Out There?* is thorough and scientifically informative, while still engaging and accessible. If recent headlines and current scientific discoveries have piqued your interest in the possibility of alien life in the universe, get this book *now*."

–J. Warner Wallace, cold-case detective, Senior Fellow at the Colson Center for Christian Worldview, and author of *Cold-Case Christianity, God's Crime Scene, Forensic Faith,* and the accompanying children's books

"As a frequent traveler and speaker in many countries, I am amazed at how often I or my colleagues are asked questions about life on other planets! In an age that struggles with belief in God or the gods, it is a sincere point of curiosity as to whether or not there is something *out there*. These are not trivial questions, nor can they be pushed aside as if only relevant to some stargazing child or nerd. They point to the deepest longings of the heart and the hungers we all have for transcendence, meaning, and truth. I cannot think of anyone better qualified than Jeff Zweerink to engage these issues in a serious and practical manner. He loves science, he loves the truth, and he is a great communicator. I hope you will read this book and pass it along to your curious friends. Is there life out there? The answer may be more surprising than you think!"

–Stuart McAllister, PhD, global support specialist, Ravi Zacharias International Ministries

"Here is a book that is as much fun to read as it is informative. Writing in a style that is (mostly) accessible to laypeople, Zweerink addresses questions about the universe that have been raised by recent astronomical di... multiverse exist? Could earth have been seeded by ... vay to know if life exists on exoplanets? And what's ... net? Zweerink answers these questions and more. ... ist, he provides his answers from the perspective ...

..., senior professor of theology, Southeastern Baptist Theological Seminary

JEFF ZWEERINK

IS THERE
LIFE
OUT THERE?

A Christian Astrophysicist Answers Common Questions
about the Search for Life-Friendly Planets

Cover design: 789, Inc.
Illustrations: Sean Platt and Phil Chien
Interior layout: Christine Talley

Unless otherwise identified, all Scripture quotations taken from the Holy Bible, New International Version ®, NIV®. Copyright ©1973, 1978, 1984, 2011 by Biblica, Inc.TM Used by permission of Zondervan. All rights reserved worldwide. www.zondervan.com The "NIV" and "New International Version" are trademarks registered in the United States Patent and Trademark Office by Biblica, Inc. TM

Printed in the United States of America

For more information about Reasons to Believe contact (855) REASONS / (855) 732-7667 or visit www.reasons.org.

For Lisa Zweerink and our five beautiful children

Contents

Illustrations

List of Figures

List of Tables

Acknowledgments

Family and friends who know me best understand that I am not one for much sentiment. I like to think it goes without saying that writing, editing, and publishing a book is a team effort and that the many people who worked tirelessly know how valuable they are to me. Nonetheless, I'd like to express my thanks to just some of the people who made this work possible.

I am thankful to God for directing my path to Reasons to Believe, a workplace of gifted, passionate people. For the input of scholars Hugh Ross, Fazale Rana, Ken Samples, and AJ Roberts. For Tuesday lunches spent gleaning wisdom and support from Dr. Dave Rogstad. For editor Joe Aguirre encouraging me to write in my voice to an audience that I care about. For editors Sandra Dimas, Bethany Garrison, Jocelyn King, and Amanda Warner who prodded me to keep going when the words came slowly and for reading and rereading my terrible jokes.

I am thankful for the many churches and youth groups who let me present the ideas contained in this book and gave me helpful, valuable feedback.

I am thankful for my wife and five kids who let me present the ideas contained in this book around the dinner table and gave me helpful, if a bit more direct, feedback.

I am thankful for the designers—cover designers Charley Bell and Richard Silva of 789, Inc., interior layout designer Christine Talley, and illustrators Sean Platt and Phil Chien—for their work in making this book look good.

I am thankful for peer reviewers Bijan Nemati, Michael Strauss, and Timothy Boyle for so patiently searching my words and ideas. I will take full credit for all errors that remain.

Above all, I must give praise to my Heavenly Father, the greatest Author of all.

Jeff Zweerink
2017

The Quest to Find Our Place in the Universe

"I shall cite evidence to show that they [extraterrestrials] have long since invaded and that their effects can be uncovered by historical research." Michael J. Crowe[1]

A young farmer stares off into the setting suns of his home planet. An assortment of peculiar aliens revel in a dimly lit cantina. A battered spaceship travels at lightspeed across a distant galaxy far, far away. And an epic rebellion against the Galactic Empire begins.

I was eight years old when I first saw *Star Wars* (or *Star Wars: Episode IV – A New Hope*, as it's now called), and I'll never forget the impression it made on me. What eight-year-old boy wouldn't find the (then) groundbreaking special effects fascinating? The film franchise's continued success at the box office and in merchandising demonstrates the widespread interest in George Lucas's alien worlds.

The public's enthrallment with alien worlds doesn't stop there. The multitude of blockbuster films featuring otherworldly beings reveals our fascination with life out there in the universe. A short, long-necked, Reese's Pieces–eating visitor finally figures out how to "phone home." James Tiberius Kirk captains the starship *Enterprise* on missions seeking to "boldly go where no man has gone before." And Agents J and K work for a top secret organization that tracks all alien activity on Earth, making sure to keep any evidence of aliens' existence under wraps.

Whether or not they exist, aliens have already invaded human culture. But what sparked people's fascination with aliens?

When Did People Begin Thinking about Aliens?

Today, a large group of scientists and laymen under the umbrella of SETI—the Search for Extraterrestrial Intelligence—continually observes the skies and crunches data, looking for radio signals that would indicate the presence of intelligent life on some distant planet. But the search for aliens began long ago. (The only new aspect is that it extends beyond the solar system.)

In the late 1800s, a prominent Italian astronomer named Giovanni Schiaparelli reported finding evidence of intelligent life much closer to home. He purportedly observed fine lines crisscrossing the surface of Mars and interpreted these lines as canals that moved large quantities of liquid, presumably water. His imagery also included tracks, akin to those used by trains on Earth, that were, from his perspective, certainly built by intelligent inhabitants to transport goods across the Martian landscape. (Of course, having observed Mars through rovers and stationary equipment, scientists now know that no canals or seas or train tracks exist on the surface of the planet.)

Perhaps people's fascination with aliens began a couple hundred years earlier, starting in earnest in the 1600s when Galileo Galilei first turned a telescope to the heavens and the scientific enterprise began to flourish. Galileo (a Christian) strongly argued against any Earth-like life existing elsewhere.[2] In contrast, Johannes Kepler (Galileo's contemporary and also a Christian) envisioned other worlds teeming with life. He thought the Moon, the "earths" orbiting Jupiter (the moons Galileo discovered), and even Jupiter itself hosted its own biosphere.[3]

It can be argued (as done by many scholars) that talk of extraterrestrials began in the 1500s with the work of Nicolaus Copernicus. According to this line of reasoning, Copernicus's heliocentric model of the solar system removed Earth from the central location in the universe. In Copernicus's time, this was not a demotion in Earth's status but a promotion![4] With the Sun as the center of the solar system (and our solar system one among many in the universe), it seems almost natural to speculate on the existence of life around those distant suns. But the discussion started much earlier.

In the 1400s, philosopher and theologian William Vorilong addressed the question of whether life beyond Earth could be reconciled with foundational Christian doctrines. Specifically regarding the incarnation and atonement of Jesus Christ, Vorilong argued that if such life existed, it would not fall into sin (as did Adam and Eve in the garden of Eden). However, he also asserted that Christ's death on Earth was sufficient to redeem inhabitants of other worlds, but "it would not be fitting for Him to go into another world that he must die again."[5]

Even earlier, prominent theologians and philosophers like Thomas Aquinas (1225–1274), Aristotle (385–323 BC), Plato (428–348 BC), Augustine (354–430), and Origen (185–254) weighed in on the question of a "plurality of worlds" with both sides of the issue advocated by highly regarded thinkers. Although classical scholars date the origin of the extraterrestrial discussion in Western thought to the fifth century BC, given human fascination with the topic, I would not be surprised to find that Adam and Eve had heated discussions about aliens.

Thousands of years of inquiry have not settled the matter of whether life exists elsewhere—at least not yet. Scientific advances since the mid 1990s opened the door to answer one part of the question: Do other planets like Earth exist and, if so, are they hospitable to life?

Finding Planets beyond the Solar System

Excluding highly questionable claims of UFO sightings, scientists have not found any evidence of physical life beyond planet Earth. Assuming our galaxy hosts a vast array of life, many scientists have offered reasons for why we have no evidence for that life.[6] Like *Star Trek*'s Prime Directive (of nonintervention), perhaps superadvanced civilizations have visited us in undetectable ways. Maybe they chose to hide from our telescopes, or we cannot yet recognize their signals. Or maybe any number of reasons prevent intelligent life from residing anywhere but here on Earth.

Astronomer Frank Drake provided a useful framework for answering why Earth hosts the only known life in the universe. He developed the Drake equation[7] (see page 16) that breaks down the complex question of finding extraterrestrial civilizations into a handful of more manageable factors that scientists can address. Generally, one assumes that the detection will arise through electromagnetic emissions because we use telescopes to search for evidence of any existing civilizations.

To determine all these factors will require research in disciplines including astronomy, physics, planetary science, geology, biology, biochemistry, and many others. In fact, scientists have formed a discipline called *astrobiology* that encompasses the specific aspects of all these other disciplines that pertain to life's existence. A major component of astrobiological research entails the search for other planets that might host life. Until the mid 1990s, this was a "data-free" endeavor—if one excluded the planets and moons of the solar system.

That changed in November 1995 when two astronomers published a paper

What Is the Drake Equation?

$$N = R^* \cdot f_p \cdot n_e \cdot f_l \cdot f_i \cdot f_c \cdot L$$

N: the number of detectable civilizations throughout the Milky Way Galaxy

R*: the average rate of formation of stars suitable for intelligent life

f_p: the fraction of stars suitable for intelligent life that have planetary systems

n_e: the average number of planets in those planetary systems

f_l: the fraction of those planets that develop life

f_i: the fraction of those life-forms that develop intelligence

f_c: the fraction of those intelligent life-forms that develop advanced civilization resulting in signals sent into space

L: the length of time those civilizations emit the signals into space

in *Nature* demonstrating the existence of a planet orbiting the star called 51 Pegasi.[8] Analysis showed this exoplanet (a planet outside our solar system) had an orbital period of 4 days. Though it looked more like Jupiter than Earth, it represented a milestone in that it was the first time astronomers had detected an exoplanet orbiting a star similar to the Sun.[9]

Over the next few years, astronomers found a steady trickle of exoplanets (most similar to the original find) and the trickle grew to a stream. Now, more than 20 years later, the number of known and potential exoplanets is in the thousands!

Before finding any exoplanets, scientists generally believed that most planetary systems would resemble the solar system. To their surprise, the exoplanet catalog shows many ways planets form that look different from ours. Jupiter-sized planets orbit close to their parent stars. Some significant fraction of these Jupiter-sized planets orbit in the opposite direction than the host star spins. And, reminiscent of the binary sunset in *Star Wars*, some exoplanets orbit around multiple stars.

Astronomers have not yet found a planetary system that looks like ours. Moreover, unless some fortuitous circumstances arise, they currently do not possess the sensitivity to detect such a system. However, they *have* detected Earth-sized objects orbiting at a distance where liquid water could exist. Thus,

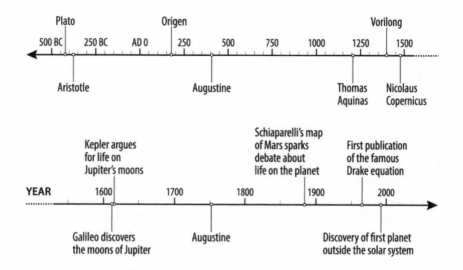

Figure I.1: Brief Timeline of Philosophy and Scientific Discoveries

even before this field of exoplanet detection has matured beyond toddlerhood, it provides insight into the values of a number of factors in the Drake equation. With this new insight, we can hope to inch closer to resolving the question people have wondered about for centuries: Is there life out there?

How This Book Is Organized

Each chapter in this book addresses one question relevant to the search for another planet that could support life. Throughout the chapter, I discuss the latest scientific findings pertinent to the question. Each chapter can stand alone as a question answered, but the book is meant to be read in its entirety, chapter by chapter (there are 20). We are on a quest to find life "out there," and each chapter builds on the previous one. See the table of contents for the guide to the journey. If some material is especially technical, don't worry too much. No chapter is long. Plus, I have included a few "takeaways" at the end of almost all the chapters to help recall important points.

But What about God?

One unique contribution of this book is that it seeks to address how exoplanet research interacts with the ongoing dialogue between scientific advance and the Christian faith. Questions like "Is Earth designed uniquely to support life?"

and "Will Christianity be debunked if we find alien civilizations?" figure prominently in this dialogue. Unfortunately, many who engage in such interactions portray them as more of a war than a dialogue.

One of my first interactions with this hostility occurred during an English class in my first year of college. My professor assigned *The Star* by Arthur C. Clarke for discussion in class. (Please read the tale for yourself. The author tells a more gripping story than any summary I could offer.[10])

The story tells of a group of non-Christian scientists and a Christian who embark on a mission to explore a distant supernova. As they approach the remnants of the dead star, they find a planet and, upon investigating the planet's surface, also a memorial to an advanced civilization extinguished by the supernova event. The team uncovers the lore and history of the people on the distant planet. However, after a closer look at the timing of the supernova and distance from Earth, the Christian comes to a conclusion that shakes the foundation of his faith. This supernova was the star that announced the birth of Christ to the wise men!

How could God sacrifice this remarkable race just to proclaim the birth of his Son on Earth? To be clear, the tapestry woven by Clarke faces a number of scientific and theological problems, but the key point reflects a common question: Can faithful and devoted followers of the God of the Bible truly integrate their scientific understanding of this universe with the words of Scripture?

The final chapters of *this* book seek to provide such an integration, at least related to the issues surrounding planets outside the solar system and the possibility of finding life on one of those planets.

More than 2,000 years after scholars first started writing down their thoughts on life beyond Earth, the final answer remains elusive. However, the scientific advances over the last couple of decades provide many details that fill out the discussion. Let's begin with a big-picture overview of how life got started in the universe.

Chapter 1

The Big Picture

Life abounds on planet Earth! We are familiar with numerous life-forms—like people, animals, and insects. Using microscopes we can see a host of bacterial and viral organisms. Digging in the dirt reveals bones of enormous dinosaurs. Life takes many different shapes and sizes and has varied life spans. Scientists find life in virtually every environment where they suspect life could exist and even in many environments they once thought inhospitable to life. Some bacteria thrive in boiling water, bubbling tar, extremely dry deserts, frozen glaciers, rocks two miles below Earth's surface, and in environments with radiation levels that would destroy cockroaches. Why is Earth so hospitable to life?

In the beginning, neither the universe nor Earth when it first formed could host life. But, as scientists have discovered over the past few decades, the universe and Earth underwent significant changes that now permit life so readily on Earth. This ubiquity of life on Earth can make it seem like life should also abound in the universe. To evaluate the possibility of life "out there," it is useful to remember what transpired from the beginning of the universe until today. This chapter provides an overview that briefly describes the important, life-critical transitions that occurred since the creation of the universe.

Creation of the Universe

Our universe began almost 14 billion years ago.[1] During the earliest moments of the universe, it expanded at a tremendous rate. This period of inflation ended with two important consequences. First, the total amount of "stuff" that astronomers can see (around 100 billion trillion stars spanning a sphere roughly 46 billion light-years in radius[2]) constitutes just a small fraction of the amount of stuff out there. Second, as this epoch of inflation ended, it released an enormous amount of energy that heated the universe to unfathomable temperatures. As the universe cooled from this hot, dense state, a number of transitions important to the discussion of extraterrestrial (ET) life occurred.

First Few Minutes

During the first fractions of a second, the quantum gravitational force governing all the interactions in the universe separated into the distinct forces we see at work today—the gravitational, strong nuclear, electromagnetic, and weak nuclear forces. The gravitational force (the force between objects with mass) affects how the universe expands, the sizes and lifetimes of stars, and the atmospheres of planets. The strong nuclear force (the force keeping protons and neutrons bound inside a nucleus) influences the amount of various elements of the universe in two ways. First, during the initial few minutes of the universe, temperatures and densities are high enough for hydrogen (the lightest element) to fuse into heavier elements. Second, stars also experience conditions where lighter elements (like carbon) fuse with helium to make heavier ones (like oxygen). The electromagnetic force affects anything with charge as well as all forms of light. Consequently, it affects the sizes and lifetimes of stars as well as every chemical interaction necessary for life. The weak nuclear force determines how heavier elements decay into lighter elements. It also plays a critical role in how stars fuse hydrogen into helium and how heat is generated in Earth's interior (radioactive decay produces lots of heat).

At the end of four minutes, the universe had cooled significantly—its temperature dropping below one billion degrees. Enough hydrogen had fused into helium that these two elements comprised 75% and 25%, respectively, of all the nuclei in the universe. Only trace amounts of beryllium and boron existed.

Cosmic Microwave Background Radiation

Not much changed over the next 400,000 years except that the universe continued to cool. Around 380,000 years, the temperature fell low enough that the hydrogen and helium nuclei could combine with the surrounding electrons to form atoms. As the atoms formed, they emitted a specific distribution of light that we now measure as the cosmic microwave background (CMB) radiation. Scientists use this light to determine the age, mass density, expansion rate, size, and many other important characteristics of the universe.

First and Later Generations of Stars

Over the next billion years, a couple of big changes occurred. About 200 million years after the universe began, the most significant one happened when

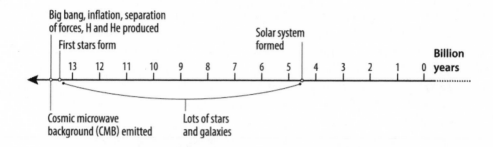

Figure 1.1: Important Events in the History of the Universe

stars began forming. For the first time since the early minutes of the universe, conditions for producing elements heavier than hydrogen and helium existed. These original stars contained hundreds of times more mass than that of the Sun. Consequently, they burned their nuclear fuel quickly (within a few million years), exploded in dramatic supernova events, and scattered copious amounts of elements such as heavy uranium, neptunium, and plutonium into the material that would form future stars.

During the next few hundred million years galaxies also started to form. Later generations of stars formed from the ashes of the first stars. This buildup continued to enrich galaxies with the heavier elements throughout the three generations of stars that astronomers have identified. While gas giant planets can form around stars with lesser amounts of heavy elements, only this third generation of stars had sufficient quantities of carbon, oxygen, uranium, and plutonium to make planets capable of supporting life.

Formation of the Sun and Planets

Four-and-a-half billion years ago, a supernova explosion sent a shock wave into a cloud of gas. The pressure from the shock wave compressed the gas in the cloud, causing it to collapse, making the Sun and planets in the process. For 5 to 10 million years, the planets grew by gathering gas, dust, and ice until the wind emitted by the young Sun drove all the planet-growing material from the solar system. Two critical events happened over the next 500 million years. First, around 100 million years after Earth formed, a large, Mars-sized object collided with Earth. This impact event increased Earth's mass, added radioactive elements to Earth's interior, and—most importantly—made the Moon.[3] Second, during this 500-million-year period, Jupiter, Saturn, Uranus, and Neptune migrated from their places of origin to their current locations. This period of migration moved the gas giants farther from the Sun and likely caused Neptune and Uranus to switch positions.

Life's Development on Earth

Earth's original atmosphere contained no free oxygen, little (if any) land rose above the oceans, and large objects frequently collided with the planet. In spite of this rather hostile environment, studies show that life on Earth dates back almost 4 billion years ago. Scientists have found fossilized life from 3.5 billion years ago and chemical evidence from another 300 million years earlier. Admittedly, this life was simple compared to the standard of life on Earth today.

As mentioned, the orbits of the gas giants changed significantly. The rate of comets and asteroids impacting Earth (and other rocky bodies like Mars, the Moon, Mercury, and Venus) dramatically increased as the gas giant planets migrated to their current positions. Many of these impact events probably sterilized Earth's surface, but this period of bombardment also cleared the solar system of debris. Subsequently, the frequency of objects colliding with Earth decreased by a factor of 1,000. Evidence indicates that life appeared on Earth in abundance shortly after this Late Heavy Bombardment (or LHB, as scientists refer to this period).

Over the next 2–3 billion years, the amount of land covering Earth's surface increased. As scientists dated the formation of continental rocks, they discovered that the rocks clustered around a few ages, specifically 1.2, 1.9, 2.7, and 3.3 billion years ago.[4] The added growth of continental landmass brought new environments for life to thrive and provided a thermostat that regulates Earth's temperature (see chapter 5). This thermostat function featured prominently when photosynthetic organisms started producing enough free oxygen so that Earth's oceans and atmosphere began to contain a permanent oxygen component roughly 2.5 billion years ago.

The Cambrian Explosion

One of the most dramatic changes in the history of life on Earth occurred about 540 million years ago. During a geologically short period of time, a wealth of multicellular organisms showed up in the fossil record in an event referred to as the Cambrian explosion. Before this time the fossil record showed only the presence of single-celled life that occasionally organized into colonies. While

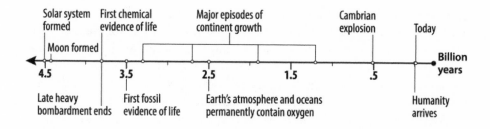

Figure 1.2: Important Events in the History of Earth

animal life has changed significantly over the last 540 million years, almost all the different body plans (the distinguishing feature of the different phyla) appeared during the Cambrian explosion.

Humanity Arrives

Humanity, the most unique form of life ever seen on Earth, arrived much more recently. Fossil, genetic, and archaeological evidence indicate that human beings started living about 100,000 years ago. Although other animals share physiological features with humans, we are the only creatures that have both a deep-seated capacity to relate to one another and an awareness of our own existence. One way this awareness manifests itself is through a universal sense that God exists and that we must figure out how to properly relate to him.

A Match with Genesis

Even this brief description demonstrates a correspondence between our best scientific understanding of Earth's history and the creation account given in Genesis 1. Both begin with the origin of the universe (the big bang, see Genesis 1:1) before moving to the initial stages of planet Earth (which is hostile to life at this time, see Genesis 1:2). Early Earth's bombardment period transformed the atmosphere so that light reached the planet's surface (Genesis 1:3–5, the first day brings the day-night cycle to the surface). It also brought water recognized as critical to a stable water cycle (Genesis 1:6–8). In the middle of Earth's history (Genesis 1:9–13, day three of six), most of the continents formed, which would also allow plants to grow. Complex, multicellular life appeared explosively during the Cambrian explosion (mirroring day five in Genesis 1:20–23). Humanity arrived very recently (at the end of day six, Genesis 1:24–31). Obviously, scientists have learned far more about natural history than the snapshot given in Genesis 1. However, it is remarkable that a book authored thousands of years ago—before humanity developed a thriving scientific enterprise—got the important details of Earth's history correct![5]

With this overview in mind, we can now focus attention on the physical characteristics of exoplanets and what they reveal. Will the latest scientific discoveries show that other planets are capable of harboring life? Our journey begins by considering something as routine as Earth's orbit.

 Takeaways ⎯⎯⎯⎯⎯⎯⎯⎯⎯⎯⎯⎯⎯⎯⎯⎯⎯⎯⎯⎯

- The ubiquity of life on Earth can make it seem like it should also abound in the universe.

- In spite of hostile conditions, life on Earth dates back to almost four billion years ago.

- During a geological instant known as the Cambrian explosion, a wealth of multicellular organisms showed up in the fossil record.

- Humanity arrived late on the scene—approximately 100,000 years ago—and with unique capacities for relationship and self-awareness.

- The fact that the Genesis account corresponds to our best scientific understanding of Earth's history provides evidence that the Bible is not just a product of human authors.

Chapter 2

What Would a Day on Another Planet Look Like?

"Let's call it a day." "The difference is like night and day." "We'll take it day by day." "Go ahead. Make my day!"

These common expressions reflect a restricted understanding of the word "day" as being what we experience here on Earth. Specifically, as the Earth rotates, the Sun "rises" in the east, "sets" in the west, and repeats the process every 24 hours. (More accurately, Earth rotates on its axis every 23 hours, 56 minutes, 4.09 seconds, and it takes 365.242 of those days to complete one orbit around the Sun.) But what would a day look like on other planets?

Mercury, Venus, and Mars

Though Mercury, Venus, and Mars are our nearest neighbors, their "days" and "years" lack any semblance of what we experience here on Earth. Because Mercury orbits closer to the Sun than Earth, it experiences a rather odd relationship between its day and year. Earth orbits the Sun every 365 days. Mercury takes only 88 days (24 hours, unless otherwise noted). Mercury's proximity to the Sun means that the planet is nearly tidally locked. An example of a complete tidal locking is the Moon with Earth. Because the Moon is tidally locked with Earth, the same side of the Moon always faces Earth. The nearly tidal locking of Mercury means that instead of the same side always facing the Sun, Mercury rotates on its axis three times for every two orbits around the Sun. This might sound like each Mercurian year (orbit around the Sun) contains 1.5 Mercurian days (from sunrise to sunrise). However, when viewed from the surface, one Mercurian day would occur every two Mercurian years.

A day on the surface of Venus looks bizarre in other ways. Being in between Mercury and Earth, Venus orbits the Sun once every 225 days. However, Venus rotates very slowly. Even though Venus and Earth are similar in size, a point on

Venus's equator moves with a speed of 4 miles per hour (mph) compared to 1,040 mph for a point on Earth's equator. Additionally, it rotates backwards on its axis (retrograde in astronomy parlance) meaning that the Sun would rise in the west and set in the east. The slow retrograde rotation of Venus means that one Venusian year lasts just under two Venusian days. Of course, sunrise and sunset are moot issues concerning Venus because the thick atmosphere prevents any sunlight from reaching the surface!

Venus and Mercury share the feature of long days compared to Earth, and they both orbit closer to the Sun. Consequently, both planets experience hellish temperatures. Although the nighttime side of Mercury cools to -279°F, well below the freezing point of water, the Sun-facing side of Mercury climbs as high as 801°F. And Venus's dense carbon-dioxide atmosphere keeps its surface temperature a toasty 864°F. At these temperatures, this book would spontaneously erupt into flames—if these planets had any oxygen in their atmospheres.

When compared to Mercury and Venus, Mars looks far more like Earth. The greater distance from the Sun means that Mars takes 687 days to orbit, but the Martian day lasts about 40 minutes longer than an Earth day. The nearly vertical rotation axis of Mercury and Venus results in no seasonal changes for these two planets. The axial tilt of Mars (25°) resembles Earth's (23.5°) so Mars has seasonal changes like Earth, except they last almost twice as long. Although the atmosphere of Mars corresponds to the one on Venus (96% carbon dioxide, 4% nitrogen and argon), even the atmospheric pressure atop Mount Everest exceeds the value on Mars's surface by a factor of 50.

By sending probes and using powerful telescopes, scientists have studied the planets in our solar system in great detail. Yet when we consider exoplanets, the amount of knowledge falls significantly. Scientists know quite a bit about the host stars, but little about the exoplanets themselves. Typically the extent of knowledge includes the exoplanet orbits, the physical size (mass and/or diameter), the amount of stellar radiation received, and (in specific instances) some details about the gases in the atmosphere. Nonetheless, what we do know is that these exoplanets showcase even *more* extreme examples of days than those in our solar system.

A Flood of Planetary Discoveries

In 1992 astronomers discovered the first confirmed planets outside our solar system, naming them PSR B1257+12b and PSR B1257+12c.[1] The initials "PSR" stand for "pulsar" because the planets orbit an unusual star called a pulsar. Pulsars result from stars massive enough to undergo a supernova explosion at the end of their life. The supernova compresses the material at the center of the star to enormous densities, leaving either a black hole or a neutron star. A neutron star generally has a mass similar to the Sun, with that mass squeezed into a radius of less than 10 miles. Usually, the neutron star also spins rapidly (as fast as hundreds of rotations a second) and gives off beams of light. If those beams of light repeatedly sweep across Earth as the neutron star spins, astronomers detect the signal as a pulsar (think "pulsating star"). Researchers used the precise timing exhibited by pulsars to find the two planets in this case. The discovery of planets around such a bizarre star was the first of many unexpected discoveries that show just how extraordinary our solar system seems—at least so far.

Brief Solar System Survey
The Sun is an "ordinary" star in that the fusion of hydrogen into helium in its core ultimately powers the light coming from its surface. This fusion started nearly 4.6 billion years ago, and scientists expect it to continue for another 5 billion years. In astronomical terms, this makes the Sun a "main sequence" star. Four rocky planets—Mercury, Venus, Earth, and Mars—reside closest to the Sun and follow nearly circular orbits around the Sun. An asteroid belt, which looks like the remains of a planet that never formed, contains around 1 million objects larger than 1 kilometer with orbits from 2 to 3.5 times the radius of Earth's orbit (defined as 1 astronomical unit or AU). Beyond the asteroid belt, the four gas giants—Jupiter, Saturn, Uranus, and Neptune—also orbit in nearly circular paths. The Kuiper Belt and other trans-Neptunian objects and the distant Oort cloud complete the major components of the solar system.

Two other characteristics of the solar system warrant mention. First, observations for hundreds of years demonstrated that all the planets in the solar system revolve around the Sun in the same plane. Second, the Sun rotates on its axis—an axis perpendicular to the plane in which the planets orbit. Furthermore, all the planets orbit in a prograde fashion; that is, in the same direction that the Sun rotates. Given the constraints on how planets form (see chapter 11), basic physical principles seem to demand that planets orbit in the same plane with prograde motion.

Before 1992, most scientists believed that the solar system represented the normal configuration for planets. They saw no special significance to having nine planets (Pluto was later demoted to a "dwarf planet") or in the locations of the orbits in the plane. The *composition* of any discovered planets might differ from those in the solar system. And asteroid belts might be smaller, larger, or nonexistent. Yet the basic layout of a star orbited first by rocky planets, then

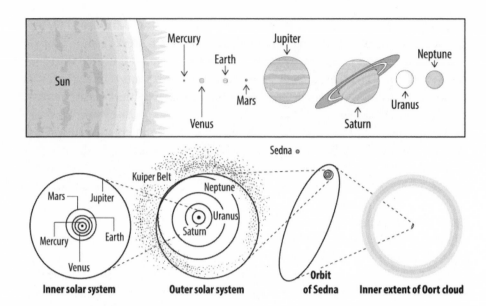

Figure 2.1: The Solar System
Top: Sun and planets to scale. Bottom: Distances to scale.

by gas giants, all in nearly circular, prograde orbits, was expected for any planetary system. The observations since then demonstrated the naïveté of that expectation.

The String of Unexpected Discoveries
Finding the first planet orbiting a Sun-like star. Though astronomers always thought planets outside our solar system existed, the first discovery of a planet orbiting a Sun-like star, an exoplanet, happened in 1995. Two astronomers at the Geneva Observatory monitored a star called 51 Pegasi for 18 months starting in April 1994. In late 1995, their data clearly showed the presence of a planet, named 51 Pegasi b, with about half the mass of Jupiter and orbiting the star in a nearly circular path.[2] In our solar system, Jupiter orbits the Sun at a distance of just over 5 AU and takes nearly 12 years to complete an orbit. 51 Pegasi b orbits its host star at a distance 100 times closer and takes just over 4 days to complete an orbit. 51 Pegasi b's proximity to its host star results in a surface temperature exceeding 1800°F! Astronomers have since discovered many of these "hot Jupiters."

Finding the second planet orbiting a Sun-like star. Just over a year after the discovery of 51 Pegasi b, astronomers found a second planet in a surprising configuration. Two teams operating at the McDonald and Lick Observatories monitored the star 16 Cygni B for signatures of a planetary companion. Their searches found a planet with a mass 50% larger than Jupiter's with an 800-day orbital period.[3] While this planet appears more similar to Jupiter than 51 Pegasi b, the shape of its orbit is far from circular. Measurements give an eccentricity of 0.69 for 16 Cygni Bb, meaning that its orbit brings the planet as close as 0.5 AU from its host and takes it as far as 2.8 AU. Such a large variability in its distance from the star will cause enormous temperature changes. Adding to the oddity of this planet, the host star resides in a triple star system. Two of the stars, 16 Cygni A and C, orbit each other at a distance of 73 AU, and 16 Cygni B orbits this pair at a distance of 860 AU.

Finding planets orbiting multiple stars. In 2011, a team of scientists announced the discovery of Kepler-16b. Studies of this exoplanet revealed that it orbited two stars, one with a mass two-thirds that of the Sun and the other with one-fifth the mass.[4] Kepler-16b takes around 229 days to orbit the binary system but has a mass similar to Saturn. This was not the first planet discovered to orbit a binary system, but the first has a much less memorable name (PSR B1620-26 b) and contains a white dwarf and a neutron star. The stars orbited by Kepler-16b would look more similar to the ones in the iconic scene from *Star Wars* where Luke watches the binary sunset of an orange and red star. The total radiation Kepler-16b receives from the stars dips by almost 15% every 41 days as the smaller star partially eclipses the larger star. The dip in radiation lasts for a couple of hours and likely causes variations in the planet's temperature and atmospheric structure.

Finding planets not orbiting any star. After two decades of planet hunting (and finding), the number of planets outside the solar system numbered in the few hundreds. Many of the techniques (see chapter 8) used to find planets look for the effects of the planet on the host star. However, the gravitational lensing method only requires that an object (like a planet or star) cross the path between the observatory and a more distant star. Such an arrangement will cause a magnification of the distant star's light. The amount of magnification and how long it lasts enable a determination of the intermediate object's mass. As astronomers scanned the heavens using this technique, they made the surprising discovery that many rogue planets wander about the Milky Way Galaxy (MWG) without orbiting any host star. The data indicates that there may be twice as many rogue planets similar in mass to Jupiter as there are stars in the

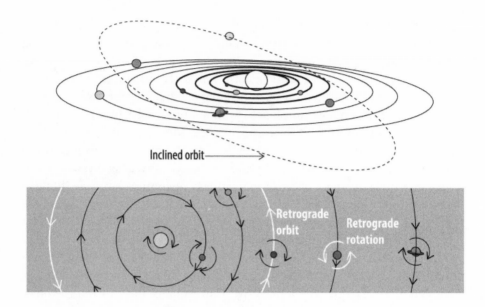

Figure 2.2: Inclined and Retrograde Orbits

MWG[5] (although the number may be much larger[6]).

Finding planets orbiting in the wrong plane and the wrong direction. Astronomers routinely measure the rotation axes of distant stars. As planet-hunting technology matured, astronomers could extract more information about exoplanets such as orbital plane and orbital direction. Starting in 2009, exoplanet searches began finding planets with highly inclined orbits. They even found planets with retrograde orbits—where the planet revolves in the opposite direction of the host star's rotation.[7]

Finding a whole different kind of planet. Perhaps the most surprising find was related to a type of planet not present in our solar system. We have rocky planets with masses approaching that of Earth, and we have gas giants as small as Uranus (about 15 times the mass of Earth), but nothing in between. As mentioned earlier, the first exoplanets discovered orbit the pulsar PSR B1257+12. Astronomers now know that the system contains three planets (designated with b, c, and d after the pulsar name) and that two of these (c and d) have masses only four times that of Earth. This small mass means that they are not gas giants. Instead, these "super Earths" likely have rocky surfaces similar to our home, but significantly more mass. Studies indicate that more than half of observed planetary systems contain a super Earth. This fact raises the question: Why doesn't our solar system have one? According to one analysis, perhaps a super Earth formed inside Mercury's orbit but gravitational interactions resulted in the planet falling into the Sun.[8]

These unexpected discoveries accomplished more than simply revealing the many different ways that a planetary system might look. They gave scientists important input to planetary formation models that help us understand what type of history a habitable planet requires.

Thus, in addition to all the conditions necessary for a "day" to take place, Earth distinguishes itself from other planets as an oddity that is just-right for life. We know life exists here on Earth. Before considering what scientists have learned about the possibility of life starting elsewhere, let's look at a different question: Could life have traveled through space to Earth?

 Takeaways ————————————————————————

- Days on planets in our solar system look far different from Earth days, but from what scientists know about exoplanets to date, they showcase even *more* extreme examples of days.

- Before 1992 most scientists believed that our solar system's configuration of (now) eight planets and their basic orbits represented the norm for other planetary systems.

- A string of extrasolar planet discoveries has revolutionized planet formation models and helped scientists understand what type of history a habitable planet requires.

Chapter 3

Can Life Move around in the Universe?

How do you travel to a distant planet orbiting another star? The *Millennium Falcon* would simply make a jump to lightspeed. In the *Star Wars* universe, it's never really explained how lightspeed works, but it seems to depend on entering some hyperspace beyond the usual three spatial dimensions of our universe. In the *Star Trek* universe, the captain of the *Enterprise* would plot a course and engage the warp drives. By warping the space around the ship, the *Enterprise* could travel great distances in short times without violating the law that nothing travels *through* space faster than the speed of light. Wormholes also provide great opportunities to either explore distant worlds with the hope of saving humanity or contacting distant aliens. Clearly life can travel great distances in and around the galaxy (and even the universe) in fictional worlds, but can life move beyond our solar system here in the real world?

Scale of the Problem

In 1977, NASA launched one of its most famous space probes, Voyager 1. Over the next three years, the satellite took the most-detailed photographs then available of Jupiter and Saturn and their moons. The trajectory by Saturn's moon Titan flung the spacecraft out of the plane of the solar system and off toward interstellar space. A dozen or so years later Voyager 1 had flown farther away from the Sun than Neptune. Engineers pointed the satellite's cameras back toward the inner solar system and snapped a final set of pictures, including the one popularized by Carl Sagan showing Earth as a pale blue dot. Voyager 1 crossed one final milestone in 2012 when it reached the boundary where solar wind no longer dominates the winds from other stars. Voyager 1 had traveled more than 121 AU (or 11 billion miles) to finally reach interstellar space.[1] Aside from showcasing the impressive ingenuity of scientists and engineers, the journey of the Voyager 1 probe also helps demonstrate the problem

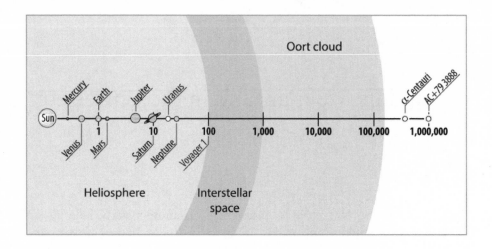

Figure 3.1: Solar System and Nearby Stellar Distances
Note logarithmic distance scale.

of interstellar travel.

Voyager 1 still holds the record as the fastest spacecraft moving away from the Sun. It took 35 years to reach interstellar space, traveling at nearly 11 miles per second (almost 38,000 mph) for most of that time. Even though Voyager 1 covers the distance from Earth to the Sun in about three months, it will take 80,000 years to cover the distance between the Sun and the nearest star (Alpha Centauri)! Voyager 1 isn't headed toward Alpha Centauri, but in 40,000 years it will pass within 1.6 light-years of a star (AC+79 3888 or Gliese 445) that is rapidly moving toward the Sun. At that time, Voyager 1 will be closer to Gliese 445 than to the Sun. Our current technology will not get us beyond the confines of our solar system, but will future advances solve those problems?

Can Future Technology Reduce the Timescales?
In order to reduce the travel times, we must reach something close to the speed of light. The usual numbers thrown around as possible travel speeds often range from 10% to 20% of the speed of light. Who knows what kind of technology such speeds might require, but physics constrains some of the factors.

Traveling at faster speeds requires larger amounts of energy, but the increase in speed does not grow in the same way as the increase in energy. For the slower speeds of everyday life and even the Voyager 1 craft, the *amount of* *energy required* to increase speed grows much faster than the speed does. Physics tells us that the energy associated with the movement, or kinetic energy, of an object (assuming no rotation) is KE = $\frac{1}{2}$ m^*v^2, where m is the mass of the object and v is the speed. Consider playing catch with a baseball. Baseballs have a mass of 0.145 kilograms (physicists do these calculations in units of kilograms, meters, and seconds). When I play catch with my kids, I typically throw the ball with speeds around 13 meters per second (m/s), or around 30 mph. So, the baseball has a kinetic energy of KE = $\frac{1}{2}$*0.145*13^2 = 12.3 joules. The same baseball thrown by a major league pitcher achieves speeds in excess of 44 m/s (around 98 mph). At these speeds, the ball has a kinetic energy of 140.4 joules. Tripling the baseball's speed increased the kinetic energy by a factor of 10. If the baseball now moves at one-tenth the speed of light (30,000,000 m/s), it has a kinetic energy of 65,000,000,000,000 joules.

For a spacecraft like NASA's *New Horizons* moving with the same speed, having a mass of 500 kg, the kinetic energy grows to 226 x 10^{15} joules. In comparison, each year the entire United States uses only 400 times more energy than this. It would take over 35 million tons of oil to produce this amount of energy, or 225 kilograms of hydrogen to produce this much energy, assuming 100% efficiency. Burning oil clearly requires too much weight in fuel. Having a mechanism that extracts the energy from fusing hydrogen into helium offers the potential to have a spacecraft where the mass of fuel is similar to the mass of the cargo. Of course, this assumes that humanity develops the capacity to operate fusion reactions and that we can extract the energy from those reactions with incredibly high efficiency. Even with all these caveats, travel to the nearest star would still take over 40 years (4.2 light-years traveling at one-tenth the speed of light). Increasing the speed any higher would dramatically increase the fuel mass.

Traveling near the speed of light poses other problems, though. Just as accelerating a craft to those speeds requires enormous amounts of energy, colliding with the debris scattered throughout interstellar space would cause tremendous damage. Space is pretty empty on average, but a journey to a neighboring star would cover a lot of space. At one-tenth the speed of light, hitting a grain of sand would impart almost 1 billion joules of energy as it rips through the hull of the spacecraft (compare that with 140 joules for a ball thrown by a major league pitcher). Even with the low density of interstellar space (anywhere from 100 to 1 trillion molecules per cubic meter), a spacecraft traveling to a nearby star basically embarks on a long game of Russian roulette. A trip through only low-density regions of interstellar space has a pretty low probability of hitting

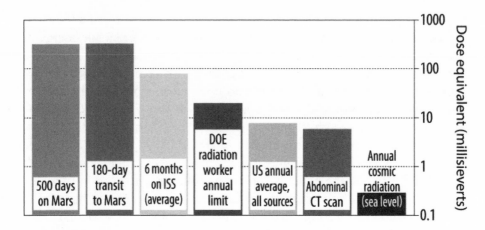

Figure 3.2: Radiation Doses by Source
Note logarithmic distance scale.

a grain of sand that would likely destroy the craft. Trajectories through higher-density regions increase the chances of impact by more than a billion.

The Radiation Problem

Whether or not the technical problems of accelerating a spacecraft to near lightspeed and shielding the craft from space dust are solvable, life on any interstellar journey faces a more serious problem. Earth's atmosphere protects the surface from a tremendous amount of damaging radiation. In every second, a 1m x 1m detector placed on top of the atmosphere would detect more than 1,000 cosmic rays with energies above 1 GeV (billion electron volts), which is 100,000 times more energy than the X-rays used by doctors. A recent trip to Mars by NASA's Curiosity rover helps quantify how exposure to this level of radiation would affect life.

A standard trip to Mars requires a roughly two-and-a-half-year commitment. The outgoing and return trips each take 180 days. However, the flights take this long only if one resides on the surface for 500 days so that Earth and Mars get to favorable locations in their orbits. During each of the flight legs, instruments on the Curiosity rover found radiation doses of 331 mSv (millisieverts). Similarly, 500 days on the surface adds another 320 mSv for a total exposure of roughly 1 Sv (sievert) for the round trip.[2] For comparison, the Nuclear Regulatory Commission states that someone exposed to 5 Sv all at once will likely die without medical treatment.[3] Although the radiation exposure is spread over two-and-a-half years, Martian astronauts are exposed to 20% of a lethal dose over this time.

More worrisome than the dose is the type of radiation encountered. Specifically, the highly energetic, high atomic number charged particles that comprise the galactic cosmic radiation (that Earth's atmosphere channels off to the poles) are incredibly effective in causing cancer (and cancers with high mortality rates). Although the exposure for a Martian trip exceeds NASA's safety limits, scientists are investigating ways to mitigate the radiation effects.[4] For example, while on Mars anything living could remain underground where the soil provides a shield against radiation.

For interstellar travel, it becomes difficult—if not impossible—to mitigate all the effects of radiation exposure. Going underground on Mars is relatively easy, but adding such shielding to a spacecraft increases the mass significantly. And the additional mass would require more fuel. Furthermore, the Voyager 1 spacecraft detected an increase of the damaging galactic cosmic rays as it exited the region influenced by the solar wind.[5] This means that travels through interstellar space cause an even larger exposure to damaging radiation.

Could Microscopic Life Survive an Interstellar Trip?
Life on Earth seems to have arisen as soon as possible. Evidence indicates that life existed at least as far back as 3.5 billion years and maybe even before 3.8 billion years. The intense bombardment of Earth from 4.1 to 3.9 billion years ago means that life showed up in abundance shortly after Earth could support life. Given this rapid appearance of life, some scientists have speculated that life arose somewhere else and was transported to Earth. Could microscopic life survive the long trip from some distant planet?

Scientists made measurements of bacterial life in Antarctic ice that helps answer this question. The ice cores contained ice ranging in age from 100,000 years to 8 million years. When trying to nurture any microbial life dormant in the ice, they found that "metabolic activity and cell viability were critically compromised with age."[6] Although the ice contained intact microbes, measurements of the length of DNA segments from ice of different ages showed a decrease from an average length of roughly 3 million base pairs down to hundreds of base pairs (in the oldest ice). Exposure to ionizing radiation from cosmic rays most likely caused the degradation. The viability of the microbes in the ice decreased by a factor of 2 for every million years of radiation exposure in the ice.

Asteroid speeds indicate that they would move through interstellar space at a rate comparable to the Voyager 1 spacecraft, meaning it would take a few hundred thousands of years to travel from some nearby star to Earth. This time is significantly less than the DNA half-life measured for Antarctic ice, so, on its own, this factor suggests a good fraction of the microbes should survive the trip. But the radiation exposure in interstellar space is tens to hundreds of times higher. The scientists studying the preservation of microbes in ice conclude "given the extremely high cosmic radiation flux in space, our results suggest it is highly unlikely that life on Earth could have been seeded by genetic material external to this solar system."[7]

Taking these conditions into account, popular sci-fi/fantasy portrayals of routine space travel featuring advanced beings seem purely the stuff of fiction. Perhaps future scientific advances will take the mystery out of space travel, and we will understand how life could move around from planet to planet. But, what requirements exist for any exoplanet that might support life? Is water the key to finding life out there? The next chapter addresses that specific question.

 Takeaways

- Travel to the nearest star at one-tenth the speed of light—assuming ideal conditions—would take over 40 years.

- Any spacecraft must be shielded from the catastrophic effects of space dust, which increase significantly as the craft nears a star.

- Radiation exposure levels for an extrasolar planetary journey would be extremely dangerous, if not lethal, for human life.

- Based on studies of preserved microbes in ice, scientists consider it highly unlikely that life on Earth could have been seeded by genetic material external to the solar system.

Chapter 4

Just How Important Is Liquid Water?

"**F**ollow the water!"

Any search for life in this universe rightfully follows NASA's mantra. Water exhibits an arguably unique set of properties that makes life possible. Although people propose other liquids like methane as a basis for life, no other known liquid meets all the criteria that life requires.

Water, the Unusual Liquid

Water so abundantly covers Earth's surface that we usually take it for granted. In fact, water stands as the most abundant liquid on Earth. Scientists estimate that our planet contains roughly 1.3 billion cubic kilometers of water (that's 340 quintillion or 3.4×10^{20} gallons). Almost 97% of this water resides in the oceans, leaving just over 3% to fill lakes, rivers, underground aquifers, glaciers, and icecaps.

Aside from its abundance, water plays countless roles in Earth's capacity to support life. Given Earth's distance from the Sun, it receives enough radiation to maintain an average global temperature of 0°F—or 32 degrees below the temperature where water freezes. However, this condition applies only if Earth has no atmosphere. In reality—and thankfully for all of us!—the greenhouse gases in Earth's atmosphere help maintain a more life-friendly average global temperature of 57°F. The dominant greenhouse gas in Earth's atmosphere is water vapor (carbon dioxide comes in a distant second).

Water's unusual (and often unique) properties facilitate life on Earth in numerous ways. Other sources provide a more thorough and exhaustive treatment[1] of those properties, so they will be only briefly described here.

Water's Anomalous Properties[2]

Water freezes from top-to-bottom. Almost all liquids increase in density as they cool. For most of its liquid temperature range, water behaves like all other liquids. However, water deviates from this standard as it approaches freezing. Below 40°F, the density decreases with temperature. Consequently, in bodies of water (like lakes, ponds, streams, rivers, seas, and oceans) the coldest water remains on top. Furthermore, when water freezes, its density decreases even further so that the resultant ice floats on top of the liquid water.

Most other liquids freeze from bottom-to-top, whereas water freezes from top-to-bottom. The ice layer on top also provides an insulating barrier that keeps any sizeable body of water from ever freezing completely. This feature of water provides stable habitats for aquatic life that no other liquid could.

Water has a large thermal capacity. Anyone who has ever swum in a cold pool or river experienced firsthand how water has a large capacity to absorb heat with little change in its temperature. In fact, the human body cannot survive longer than a couple of days in water with even a relatively mild temperature of 70°F! The high thermal capacity of water (or specific heat capacity, in more technical terms) means that the water will absorb heat from the body faster than the human body can produce heat in a sustained fashion. Additionally, steam condensing to water and water freezing to ice also release large amounts of heat.

The large thermal capacity of water plays many life-friendly roles. Because water requires lots of energy to change temperature, the oceans, lakes, and rivers on Earth's surface minimize the large temperature swings that the day-night cycle would cause. Similarly, organisms contain mostly water, so the large thermal capacity results in more stable cell temperatures. Additionally, multicellular life uses the large thermal capacity to regulate body temperatures through evaporative cooling to avoid overheating.

Liquid water sustains the proper reaction rates. Water is liquid between 32°F and 212°F (0°C and 100°C). This temperature range from 32°F and 212°F enables the proper balance between chemical stability for life-essential molecules and sufficient energy for the chemical reactions that life requires. Temperature measures the average energy available to each molecule. Molecules with more energy react more frequently than those with less energy. As a general rule, the rate of chemical reactions changes by a factor of two when the temperature changes by 18°F (or 10°C).[3]

Anyone touching a stove or even a hot cup of coffee knows the damage that an increase in energy brings. The additional energy causes reactions in the skin, resulting in the breakdown of cell membranes and other detrimental effects. Trying to introduce or sustain life in substances where the liquid temperature range is higher means that these more energetic reactions destabilize the molecules that life requires.

Colder temperatures also cause problems for life. Consider an alternative liquid proposed as a possible basis for life: liquid methane.[4] Recent studies of Saturn's moon Titan show signs of large bodies of liquid on the surface. The surface temperature of Titan (-180°C or -292°F) and its atmospheric composition (mainly nitrogen and methane), lead scientists to believe that liquid methane fills the moon's "lakes." Assuming that plausible life-chemistry based on liquid methane exists, the reaction rates in methane would, on average, proceed almost one million times *slower* than the corresponding rates on Earth. One wonders whether such slow reaction rates could even sustain life.

Liquid water provides an ideal solvent. Most introductory chemistry or biochemistry texts will identify water as the "universal" solvent. Technically speaking, a universal solvent will dissolve any substance. In reality, no such liquid exists. Water receives this designation because it dissolves more substances than any other known liquid. This feature means that water carries abundant nutrients from the highest mountains to the deepest ocean (and all the environments in between). Additionally, water dissolves many of the organics that life uses to build cells, organs, and other biologically important structures.

Water repels certain biologically important compounds. Water dissolves many, but not all, compounds. Anyone with cooking experience knows the difficulty of using water to wash anything oily or fatty. Adding dish soap that mixes with the water *and* will dissolve the oils and fats is required. Scientists use the term hydrophobic for the substances that won't dissolve in water (the term for substances that dissolve easily is hydrophilic).

The hydrophobicity of fats and oils plays an important role in living organisms. Consider how water and oil behave when "mixed." Not only do the water and oil stay separate, but also the oil segregates into clumps and even expels the water. This behavior, known as the hydrophobic effect, causes the formation of cell membranes and makes the membranes fluid and deformable.[5]

Water is liquid over a peculiar range of temperatures. If someone tried to predict the boiling point of water based on other chemically similar molecules, he would get a boiling point near -150°F![6] The periodic table groups elements with similar chemical properties in the same column. Since oxygen resides in the third column from the right, one expects sulfur, selenium, tellurium, and polonium to behave in a chemically similar fashion. A plot of the boiling points of all the "dihydride" molecules (those with two hydrogen atoms) formed from these elements shows just how odd water is.

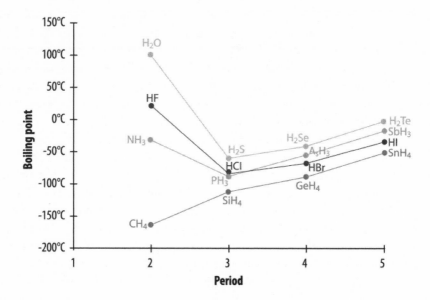

Figure 4.1: Boiling Points of Compounds Containing Specific Elements Bonded to Hydrogen
Note the unusually high boiling points for period 2 elements, especially oxygen.

Source of Water's Properties

In order to understand why water behaves the way it does requires a closer look at how atoms and molecules bond together. Although many different chemical bonds exist, the three simplest include ionic, metallic, and covalent. For purposes of this discussion, we need only a basic understanding of covalent bonding and the hydrogen bonding that occurs between water molecules.

A covalent bond between atoms occurs when the atoms share electrons. For water, this involves one oxygen atom sharing electrons with two hydrogen atoms. Usually the sharing is not equal and it depends on the elements' electronegativity; that is, how strongly the individual atoms attract electrons. The electronegativity of oxygen far exceeds that of hydrogen (and every other element except fluorine). Consequently, the shared electrons in the hydrogen-oxygen bonds associate more closely with the oxygen. This leaves the hydrogen with a net positive charge. Since like charges repel each other, one might

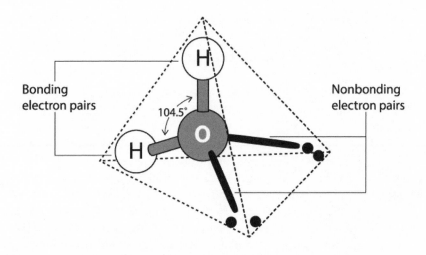

Figure 4.2: Water Molecule Configuration
The hydrogen atoms associated with the bonding electron pairs exhibit a positive charge and
the nonbonding electron pairs exhibit a negative charge.

initially think that the two hydrogen atoms would bond on opposite sides of the
oxygen, making water a linear molecule. If water had strictly covalent bonds,
it would be a linear molecule and not exhibit all these life-friendly properties.
Instead, the hydrogen and oxygen in water form more-complex bonds that
result in a bent structure to the molecule.[7] As shown in figure 4.2, the hydrogen
atoms make a 104.5° angle with one another.

This "bent" configuration of water and the electron arrangement around
the oxygen mean that various parts of the molecule exhibit a slight charge
(even though the molecule as a whole is neutral). Specifically, as mentioned
earlier, the two hydrogen atoms have a positive charge. The remaining electrons around the oxygen arrange themselves so that two other regions (that
would nearly form a tetrahedral arrangement with the two hydrogen atoms)
have a negative charge. This nonsymmetric arrangement of charge around the
water molecule leads to all its life-friendly properties.

Consider the unusually high boiling point of water compared to other
chemically similar compounds (see figure 4.1). Because of the slight positive
and negative charges exhibited by the different locations on the water molecule, each interacts with one another via hydrogen bonding.[8] Basically, the negative part of one molecule attracts the positive part of another molecule. This

Can Another Liquid Support Life?

As we know from living here on Earth, water greatly facilitates the development and advancement of life. Additional properties of water merit a brief mention.

The large thermal conductivity of liquid water (compared to any other liquid) helps distribute heat more uniformly through cells. However, the low thermal conductivity of both liquid and solid water (ice) makes a good blanket for lakes and smaller bodies of water during the winter.

The large dielectric constant of water means it easily dissociates strongly ionic compounds like salts, and it facilitates the dissolving of amino acids—the building blocks of life. The odd density profile of water (the greatest density at 4°C) helps vertically circulate water through large bodies of water. It also assists in the breakdown of rock (similar to how potholes form in cold climates) in preparation for soil formation.

The viscosity of ice is high enough to form glaciers that transform the land, but low enough that glaciers cannot segregate all the water at the poles. Liquid water's low viscosity means that animal hearts can efficiently pump blood throughout the circulatory system of a large body. However, it has enough viscosity to minimize the disruption to cells from external stresses and shocks.

Water's high surface tension allows important biomolecules and proteins to adhere to cell membranes, allowing for higher degrees of organization. When coupled with its strong interaction with various surfaces, water's high surface tension also leads to capillary action. This phenomenon draws water upwards in soil (against gravity) and enables tall plants to draw water from roots to leaves and branches.

Given all the properties of water that facilitate life on Earth, can we find any other substance to sustain life? The answer is almost certainly a resounding "No!" When considering only *one* of these many characteristics, water outranks any competitor. Where other substances perform better, adding a second characteristic puts water in a class of one again. For example, many common carbon-based compounds like ethanol (C_2H_6O), acetic acid (or vinegar, $C_2H_4O_2$), and carbon-tetrachloride (CCl_4) have a larger heat capacity than water but they do not dissolve nearly as many biologically important substances as water does.

attraction, while weaker than those between the atoms in a single molecule, is much stronger (about 10 times) than any other forces between the molecules themselves. In a pool of liquid water, the attraction of the water molecules to one another via hydrogen bonding means that it takes more energy to separate the molecules to form a gas. More energy corresponds to a higher boiling point.

The elements in the other molecules chemically similar to water—sulfur, selenium, tellurium, and polonium—have a much lower electronegativity than oxygen. Consequently, the charge distributes more uniformly on the hydrides of these elements such that they don't experience hydrogen bonding.

The Liquid That Almost Wasn't

Most of water's unusual, life-friendly properties stem from hydrogen bonding. At least it would seem so from a "classical" (as opposed to a "quantum"[9]) understanding of how atoms and molecules behave. According to this classical perspective, the atoms in a molecule of water always have the same, fixed spacing, and the molecules move in a continuous, well-specified way. Starting with this classical picture of water, modeling the atomic and molecular dynamics readily reproduces the hydrogen bonding shown from all sorts of measurements.

When chemists began modeling the interactions of water molecules, and they included the quantum effects, the models predicted that the effects of hydrogen bonding would be noticeably diminished. The Heisenberg uncertainty principle dictates that water molecules cannot have a definite position relative to one another.

Similarly, the atomic positions in the molecule suffer the same consequence. Practically speaking, this means that the atomic and molecular positions continually fluctuate, with the net effect of reducing the strength of hydrogen bonding and, more importantly, eliminating many of water's life-friendly properties.[10]

More recent modeling of water's interactions that includes the quantum effects in a more detailed and accurate way shows how two competing quantum processes balance one another to give water the properties so important to life.[11] The quantum fluctuating distances between molecules weakens the hydrogen bond. The fluctuating distances between the atoms (and the fluctuations in the bond angle, which average to 104.5°) lead to a greater separation between the slight negative and positive charges on the water molecule. (Scientists call two charges separated by some distance a dipole.) The increased distance results in the negative and positive charge seeming larger to other

Heisenberg Uncertainty Principle

According to Heisenberg's uncertainty principle, the more precisely the position of a particle is determined, the less precisely the momentum (mass times velocity) is known at this instant, and vice versa. Chemically bonded atoms and molecules require a small relative velocity, producing a reduced uncertainty in the momentum. In order to obey the uncertainty principle, the distance between the atoms and molecules must fluctuate, leading to an increased uncertainty in the position.

molecules and, consequently, a greater dipole attraction between water molecules. The more accurate models show that the increase in the dipole attraction effectively offsets the decrease in hydrogen bonding.

Experiments by another team of physicists validated this picture where two competing quantum effects produce water's properties. Water can form from two different isotopes of hydrogen: hydrogen with only one proton, and deuterium with one proton and one neutron. The extra mass of deuterium makes it less susceptible to the quantum uncertainties in bond length compared to hydrogen, meaning that the deuterium-oxygen bonds should be shorter than the hydrogen-oxygen bond. Physicists measured the bond lengths in both kinds of water by shooting a beam of neutrons through the water and seeing how they scattered. The experiments confirmed a shorter bond length in the deuterium-oxygen bonds in agreement with the "competing quantum effects" model.[12]

What Does All This Mean?
Water's set of properties makes it uniquely suited for life, and these properties arise from the strength of interactions within the molecule and with other molecules. Quantum mechanics reduces the molecular interactions in one way—by changing the probability that hydrogen will tunnel from one molecule to another. But quantum mechanics increases the molecular interactions in a completely different way—by affecting the distribution of charges within the molecule to strengthen electromagnetic attractions between molecules. The fact that this set of properties relies on two *competing* quantum effects argues that water (or any suitable life-sustaining liquid) may be unique to this universe.

In their search for life "out there," researchers would do well to follow the water. Water's features are impressive. However, a life-friendly planet needs much more than this just-right liquid. Our planet consists of large landmasses too. How did they get there? Are the processes that cause continents to form important for life? We'll tackle this question in the next chapter.

 Takeaways ───────────────────────────────

- Water, the most abundant liquid on Earth, plays countless roles in Earth's capacity to support life.

- Water's anomalous properties (at least six of them) are vital for life and stand in sharp contrast to other proposed liquids such as methane.

- Water's covalent bond structure, a nonsymmetric arrangement of charge around the water molecule, leads to all its life-friendly properties.

- Two "competing" quantum processes balance one another to give water its life-essential properties.

Chapter 5

Why Is Plate Tectonics Essential?

G rowing up in the Midwest, I thoroughly enjoyed the impressive thunder-storms during the summer months. Watching with rapt attention as lightning streaked across the sky, I then waited in anticipation for the booming thunderclap. Occasionally tornado alarms accompanied the storms. Because I've always been impressed with these displays of nature's power, I consider it a personal disappointment to have never actually seen a tornado—although I am grateful for not having to deal with the devastation one can cause. On the other hand, I have experienced a dramatically different display of nature's power. Early in the morning on October 16, 1999 (just one year after I moved to Southern California), the magnitude 7.1 Hector Mine earthquake struck. It was quite an experience trying to walk into my kids' bedroom while our house rocked like a boat on a stormy sea! As a father, I was concerned about my kids' safety. But, truth be told, as a scientist, I was fascinated by the phenomenon!

Why Does It Matter?

Earthquakes are more than just fascinating phenomena for scientists, they're important for Earth's habitability. These temblors are caused by plate tectonics, which extended Earth's capacity to support life for billions of years.

Earth's outermost layer consists of vast, massive plates that grind past each other (plate tectonics). The movement of the plates causes earthquakes, and sometimes hot, rocky material from deep inside Earth moves through cracks in these plates to produce volcanoes. Earthquakes and volcanoes have occurred throughout human history up to the present, sometimes resulting in extensive destruction.

In 2004, a major earthquake in the Indian Ocean produced a tsunami that killed more than 200,000 people.[1] Vesuvius erupted in AD 79, spewing rock and dust that killed thousands in the cities of Pompeii and Herculaneum. Around

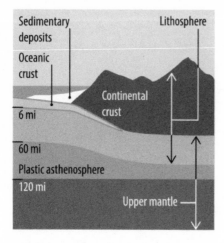
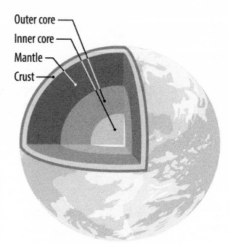

Figure 5.1: Earth's Interior

250 million years ago, a massive, million-year-long volcanic eruption in the Russian region of Siberia wiped out over 90% of the species living at the time. Given the destructive nature of volcanoes and earthquakes, one naturally asks the question: Is plate tectonics really that important to a planet's habitability? Yes! Here are some of the reasons why.

Earth's Basic Structure

Broadly speaking, Earth's interior divides into three sections (see figure 5.1). The crust (or lithosphere) extends anywhere from 3 to 125 miles below the surface. This section is composed of hard rock that forms the plates that move around the surface. Underneath the crust, the mantle reaches to a depth of 1,800 miles below the surface. The remaining ~2,200 miles to the center of the earth consist of a core made primarily of iron and nickel.

Building the Continents

Today, land covers about 30% of the globe, and the majority of Earth's diverse life relies on that land and the adjacent continental shelves. Early in Earth's history only vast stretches of ocean existed (possibly interrupted by an occasional volcanic island). For the first 1.5 billion years, Earth was largely devoid of land-mass. A crust of large plates, made from dense basalt, separated the ocean from the mantle below. Heat flowing through the mantle caused the crustal plates to move around and pushed new molten rock into the cracks between the plate boundaries.

As the newly formed ocean crust moved, two critical processes occured. First, the crust cooled and became more dense. Second, ocean water seeped into cracks and chemically altered the crust. As the plates continued to collide with one another, the denser ocean crust sank back down into the mantle. However, the chemically altered portion of the crust had a lower density and melting point. The heat generated as the plates scraped past one another melted the altered crust so that it floated to the top as continental crust.

The amount of continental crust grew over time, resulting in a large fraction of Earth's surface being covered in continents. Continents rising above the surface of the ocean started to erode under the stress of rain, wind, and other processes. The erosion carried the continental material back to the ocean plate boundaries for recycling into new continents. When the rate of erosion matched the rate of formation, the fraction of continents covering Earth's surface remained constant and led to the current continental makeup of Earth's landmass today.

Obviously this description omits many details, but the essential point remains: Without plate tectonics, no continents would have formed, and Earth would have remained a water-covered world.[2] Further, the duration of continental landmass depends on *active* plate tectonics. If plate tectonics ceased today, all of Earth's continents would disappear within about 50 million years.

The Global Thermostat

As will be discussed in chapter 14, Earth's atmosphere warms the planet well beyond the temperature expected from the amount of solar radiation received. However, the Sun's changing luminosity and the addition of photosynthetic organisms on Earth both require some mechanism to regulate the amount of greenhouse heating. The plate tectonic activity on Earth plays this role of global thermostat.

Water vapor, carbon dioxide, and methane are the dominant greenhouse gases in Earth's atmosphere. Methane reacts quickly and doesn't stay in the atmosphere very long. The productivity of methane-producing bacteria largely drives the amount of methane in the atmosphere. The largest driver of water vapor arises from temperature changes. Hotter air can hold more water vapor than colder air. In general, more water vapor causes more greenhouse heating, but water vapor also forms clouds that reflect sunlight into space. Rather than wade into the messy details of regulating methane and water vapor, let's address the amount of carbon dioxide instead.

As long as a planet has substantial landmass, the dominant mechanism for removing carbon dioxide from the atmosphere is the weathering of certain rocks and minerals (and, to a lesser degree, the burial of organisms and organic matter). Carbon dioxide in the atmosphere reacts with these minerals to produce solid materials. Erosion also exposes more of the minerals to react with the carbon dioxide in the atmosphere. Erosion processes then carry those solids down streams and rivers, eventually depositing the material on the bottom of the ocean. Thus, weathering removes carbon dioxide and incorporates it into the crust. In Earth's interior, reactions return the carbon dioxide to gaseous form that volcanic eruptions release back into the atmosphere.

Plate tectonics facilitates the release of carbon dioxide from the crustal rocks as well as replenishes the continental landmass lost through erosion and weathering. Scientists refer to this as the carbonate-silicate cycle (some minerals contain silicates that react with atmospheric carbon dioxide to form solid carbonates). The efficiency of the carbonate-silicate cycle depends on temperature. Warmer temperatures increase weathering (and the amount of carbon dioxide removed from the atmosphere), which consequently causes the planet to cool.

As the temperature cools, weathering slows (and the amount of atmospheric carbon dioxide grows), causing the planet's temperature to rise. Thus, the carbonate-silicate cycle serves as a planetary-scale thermostat. Higher temperatures also result in greater growth of complex plants (whereas lower temperatures decrease productivity). These plants also remove carbon dioxide from the atmosphere by incorporating it into solid materials that eventually find their way to the ocean floor. Thus, the presence of complex plants on Earth dramatically increases the efficiency of the carbonate-silicate cycle.

Only on a planet with long-standing, relatively constant plate tectonic activity can this global thermostat operate.

Lifting the Continents

Some of Earth's oldest (and therefore coldest) continental crust sits underneath Canada. Scientists have studied what would happen if all the continents had the same temperature as this cold, Canadian rock. According to one study, the vast majority of North America would reside underwater if the rocks making up the continental crust were cooled to the same temperature as some of the oldest crust underneath Canada. While it is not surprising that the oceans might cover coastal cities of New York, Miami, New Orleans, and Los Angeles, water hundreds of feet deep would drown even mountain cities such as Denver and Salt Lake City.[3]

It's clear that plate tectonics plays a critical role in forming and sustaining continental crust. However, as plate tectonic activity forms continents, it also heats the crust material—ensuring that those continents remain above sea level. Adding heat to rock makes the rock expand and therefore become less dense. Less-dense rock floats higher above the denser surrounding crust, meaning the surface rock sits at higher elevations. In fact, the authors of the original scientific article note, "temperature differences within the Earth's crust and upper mantle explain about *half* of the elevation of any given place in North America" (emphasis added).[4]

The bulk of life's diversity on Earth lives on the land and shallow seas of the continental crust. Less continental crust provides fewer habitats for life and also limits the capacity of plate tectonics to regulate the global temperature. While studies for other continents remain to be done, I expect similar conclusions, since the North American crust exceeds the density of continental crust averaged across the globe. The heat content of Earth's continents appears to be finely tuned to ensure Earth's habitability for human life.

Is Earth Fine-tuned for Plate Tectonics?

Most of the relevant materials in Earth's interior absorb water more readily as the depth within Earth increases (because both temperature and pressure increase with depth). One particular mineral, aluminous orthopyroxene, generally behaves as just described *except* at the pressures and temperatures corresponding to the upper part of the mantle called the asthenosphere. In this region, aluminous orthopyroxene's capacity to dissolve[5] water drops dramatically, but then increases again at even greater depths.[6] Therefore, the materials in this region of the mantle dissolve less water than those above and below it. The undissolved water likely causes the asthenosphere to partially melt.

Further, another mineral called olivine constitutes the dominant component of Earth's mantle, and the solubility of water in olivine and orthopyroxene is similar—at least in the absence of aluminum. Before this work, scientists believed that olivine controlled the water storage capacity of the earth's interior. However, the addition of aluminum increases the solubility of water in orthopyroxene by nearly a factor of 100. Scientists now know that aluminous orthopyroxene, with its unusual solubility characteristics, is the controlling material.

Why does all this matter? First, the "hydrous" melt significantly weakens the asthenosphere such that it becomes more malleable and fluid. Second, the orthopyroxene in the lithosphere (above the asthenosphere) draws the water out of the olivine, making the abundant olivine in the lithosphere more rigid. Taken together, these two effects make more rigid crustal plates that now float on a weakened and malleable asthenosphere. Consequently, Earth readily experiences plate tectonics.

These results imply that only planets of a certain size may experience plate tectonics. On planets that are too small, the location of the asthenosphere will be too deep to permit the necessary crustal plate movement. Mars and Venus illustrate this fact. Both planets show signs of plate tectonic activity in the past, but that activity ceased long ago.

Mars shows evidence of two large plates that encompass the surface of the planet. Hints of active plate tectonics do exist, but they indicate that any activity ceased within a few hundred million years after the planet formed (although sporadic plate movements might have happened much later).[7] The smaller size of Mars means that its quick cooling will shut down plate tectonics early in its history.

Venus shows evidence of catastrophic resurfacing of the planet because of a much thicker lithosphere than seen on Earth. Instead of the lithosphere fracturing into plates that move around the surface of Venus, the lithosphere forms a lid that prevents heat from escaping the interior of the planet.[8] If the heat and pressure build high enough, the molten interior breaks through the lithosphere and erupts over the surface of Venus. The last such incident happened roughly half a billion years ago.[9] Of course the lack of water on Venus also means that a far more rigid asthenosphere would bring any plate tectonics to a grinding halt.[10]

In contrast, the asthenosphere on larger planets will be shallower, resulting in much more active plate tectonics. This increased activity will dramatically increase the destructive consequences of volcanoes and earthquakes as well. As the researchers conclude, the existence of plate tectonics "is possible only in a planet with a water-bearing mantle" (that also contains sufficient aluminum).[11]

The Bottom Line

In all the discussions about what makes a habitable planet, liquid water remains the key criterion. For a given planet to have liquid water, the surface temperature must fall within a well-defined window. Scientists recognize that the atmosphere dramatically affects the surface temperature, so they perform sophisticated calculations to determine orbital distances that permit the planet to have the proper temperature. The details of these calculations almost always include the thermostat effects of plate tectonics.[12] Given this reality, we must add long-lived plate tectonic activity to the list of characteristics that a truly habitable planet must have.

It is still early in this book's quest, but one starts to wonder if Earth might be the only place meeting all of life's requirements. The odds seem to favor life on Earth, but that's because carbon-based life is the only life we know. Could life "out there" be something other than carbon based?

 Takeaways ————————————————————————————————

- Without active plate tectonics, all of Earth's continents would disappear within about 50 million years.

- Earth's constant plate tectonics serves as a global thermostat, keeping temperatures at life-friendly levels.

- The bulk of Earth's diverse life lives on land or in shallow seas of the continental crust, which is formed by plate tectonics.

- Studies of Mars and Venus (setting aside other life-essential parameters) show a lack of long-standing plate tectonic activity.

Chapter 6

Must Life Be Carbon-Based?

Some sci-fi writers imagine incredible adventures in bizarre or far-fetched otherworldly environments. One personal favorite of mine is the *Star Trek: The Next Generation* episode titled "Where No One Has Gone Before." A character referred to as "The Traveler" uses his unusual powers to transport the *Enterprise* to the outer rim of the universe, where the line between thought and reality blur. In this fascinating episode (except for the presence of Wesley Crusher) the crew encounters a creature that departs from an essential component—being carbon-based—of all Earth life.

This wouldn't be the first time *Star Trek* characters encounter non-carbon-based life. They also encounter the Crystalline Entity and Horta, silicon-based life-forms. Sci-fi and fantasy films offer plenty more examples of unusual life-forms. The Transformers, R2-D2 and C-3PO, and the shapeshifting T-1000 from *Terminator 2* represent advanced (and supercool!) sentient robots and androids. While non-carbon alien biology abounds in science fiction, must real, live organisms be carbon-based?

Why Does Carbon Work So Well for Life?

Life requires pretty complex chemistry. Carbon provides that complexity. Among the more remarkable traits of carbon is its ability to make four chemical bonds at one time. Consequently, carbon can form molecules of enormous length, and those long molecules can fold into a wide range of shapes. Life depends on these two characteristics. To understand the significance of this trait of carbon, we need to understand where elements reside in the periodic table and the different types of bonds those elements make.

Types of Chemical Bonds

Dmitri Mendeleev (considered the "father of the periodic table") assembled

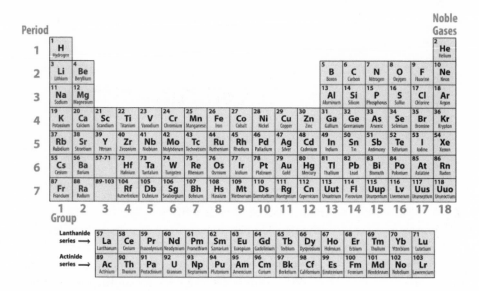

Figure 6.1: Periodic Table of the Elements
Elements in the same group exhibit similar chemical properties. Groups toward the edge of the table (1, 2, 16, 17) tend to form ionic bonds. Groups 13–15 tend to form covalent bonds. Groups 3–12 tend to form metallic bonds. Noble gases (group 18) are chemically inert.

the first version that arranged all the known elements (63 at the time) in a configuration still used today (see figure 6.1).[1] One guiding principle that allowed Mendeleev to get the ordering correct was the idea that when the elements were arranged in order of increasing mass, they exhibited a periodicity of properties. This means that elements in the same column of the periodic table will have similar chemical properties. When Mendeleev assembled his table using this guiding principle, he left gaps where he properly discerned that some elements (at least three) were not yet discovered.

Since Mendeleev first developed the periodic table, scientists have discovered the full complement of naturally occurring elements and have even made a large number of elements that are not found in nature.[2] They have also developed a more complete understanding of the chemical properties of all those elements. Some elements want to give electrons away while others want to take electrons. Other elements, like the ones in the far right column of the table, want neither to give any electrons away nor to take any additional electrons.

Scientists call these elements noble gases because they rarely (if ever) bond with other elements. Excluding the noble gases, elements toward the left of the table want to give electrons away, and elements on the right want to take electrons. The nature of the bonds between the elements depends on how the elements share their electrons (see figure 6.2).

The Ionic Bond. Elements like sodium (Na) and chlorine (Cl) make a very strong bond, which in this case means that the sodium atom basically donates an electron to the chlorine atom. Each atom in the resulting molecule (sodium chloride, NaCl, or salt), essentially acts like an ion with either a positive (Na) or negative (Cl) charge. Thus, each end of the sodium chloride molecule appears to have a large charge that strongly attracts the oppositely charged end of another sodium chloride molecule. Substances containing elements that form ionic bonds typically exist as hard, brittle crystalline solids with high melting and boiling points. Table salt provides a great example of the physical properties of a substance with many ionic bonds.

The Metallic Bond. Elements in the middle of the table, especially those in the vicinity of chromium (Cr), iron (Fe), and nickel (Ni), form bonds where the electrons are shared among a lattice of atoms. In a metallic bond, the electrons freely move from atom to atom rather than associating with just one atom or a small number of atoms. The positive nuclei of the metallic atoms float through this free-electron sea. Though many atoms associate with one another via metallic bonding, this type of bond does not lead to distinct chemical compounds with different physical properties. Metallic bonds lead to substances that are hard, shiny, and pliable. As expected, most metals (gold, aluminum, silver) and their alloys (bronze, brass, steel) form metallic bonds.

The Covalent Bond. In between the selfish ionic bond and the free-sharing metallic bond is the covalent bond. The elements in this type of bond share electrons with one another. Covalent bonds form between elements with similar tendencies to attract or give away electrons. Given the principle Mendeleev discovered for organizing the periodic table, this means that elements close together on the table tend to form covalent bonds. Since the atoms share electrons, the various sections of the resultant molecules usually have minimal charge (in contrast to ionic atoms), and as a result the molecules attract one another weakly. Substances formed from covalently bonded atoms often exist as gases, liquids, or soft solids. Nitrogen and oxygen form covalent bonds when they react to make nitrous oxide.

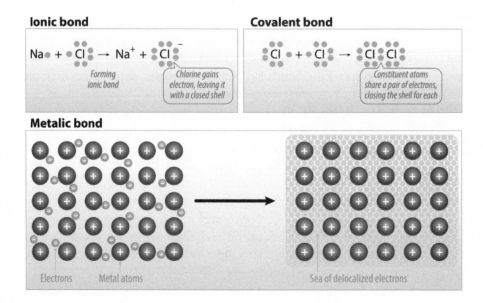

Figure 6.2: Electron Sharing in Ionic, Covalent, and Metallic Bonds

The Number of Bonds

Before addressing whether an atom other than carbon could form the basis for life, one more piece of chemistry is needed. As scientists investigated the types of reactions elements undergo, they recognized that different elements form different types of bonds and different numbers of bonds. Elements closer together on the periodic table usually form covalent bonds; more distant elements form ionic bonds. Elements toward the edge of the table form fewer bonds; those in the middle form more bonds. Consider the elements in the second row: lithium, beryllium, boron, carbon, nitrogen, oxygen, fluorine, and neon. Neon, as a noble gas, forms zero bonds. Lithium and fluorine both form one bond, although lithium wants to donate an electron to the bond and fluorine wants to take the electron. Beryllium and oxygen both form two bonds. Boron and nitrogen form three. Carbon will form four bonds!

Consider the complexity of molecules that each element could possibly form (see figure 6.3). A chain of atoms requires the element to make at least two bonds. Since lithium and fluorine both form one bond, adding an atom of

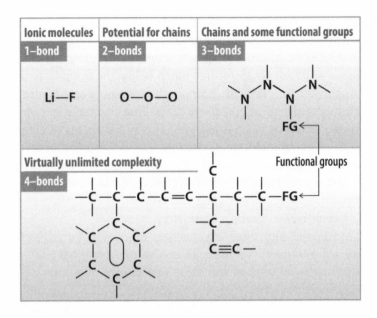

Figure 6.3: Chemical Complexity for Different Numbers of Bonds

either one ends the molecular chain. Oxygen and boron are better because they could conceivably make long chains, but the only place some other elements could join is at the two ends. In principle, nitrogen and boron could form longer, more complex chains, because other elements could join at the third bond site of each atom. However, carbon's four bonds mean that it has the capability to make the most complex set of molecules compared to any other element in the second row. By current accounting, carbon compounds number about 10 million—thousands of which are vital to life. In contrast, boron forms only thousands of compounds. Oxygen is involved in hundreds of thousands of organic compounds, but carbon forms the backbone of all those.[3]

Life-Necessary Traits of Carbon

Along with the capacity to form complex, long-chain molecules with a great diversity of chemical reactivity, carbon also meets a number of other important requirements for life. When carbon compounds react with oxygen, releasing the energy that fuels biological activity, they make carbon dioxide. In the temperature range where water is liquid, carbon dioxide is a gas, making it easy for organisms to eliminate this waste product.

The reactivity of carbon compounds is optimal in the same temperature range as liquid water. At temperatures much below the freezing point of water on Earth, the reaction rates of compounds containing carbon drop significantly. But temperatures near and above the boiling point of water increase the energy of the collisions between molecules. This added energy often breaks the carbon bonds, resulting in different compounds. Additionally, carbon (and the most prominent elements in carbon compounds, like oxygen, nitrogen, and hydrogen) ranks among the most abundant elements in the universe.

Proposed Alternatives to Carbon Chemistry

Nobody disputes the incredible effectiveness of carbon for life's chemistry, but a number of prominent scientists argue that perhaps other truly alien life-forms exist. Carl Sagan, one of the most well-known advocates of extraterrestrial life, coined the term "carbon chauvinism" to disparage the idea that only carbon forms an adequate basis for life. According to Sagan, "A carbon chauvinist holds that biological systems elsewhere in the universe will be constructed out of carbon compounds, as is life on this planet."[4]

Sagan and many others basically propose that scientists' assessment that carbon forms the only basis for life relies on a bias intrinsic to our conditions. They note that we are based on carbon and experience a small range of environments here on Earth. Given our limited experience, why should we conclude that no other chemical basis for life exists? Even with that reasoning, one must suggest some alternatives. The usual list of alternatives includes silicon, boron, sulfur, and even a combination of nitrogen and phosphorus. Let's examine the most likely alternative biochemistry to see what challenges it faces.

What about Silicon?

As mentioned previously, Mendeleev used the fact that various elements share similar chemical properties as the guiding principle to organize the elements in the periodic table. Thus, the obvious place to look for alternatives to carbon is those elements around carbon in the periodic table. Elements in the same row do not have the chemical complexity because they form fewer bonds per atom. Silicon sits immediately under carbon and exhibits many of the same chemical properties, particularly the capacity to form four covalent bonds per atom. When investigated deeper, however, silicon behaves very differently from carbon in some significant ways.

Silicon reacts strongly with oxygen. Because of its high reactivity with oxygen, silicon is not found in a free state on Earth. Instead, it forms silicon dioxide or other silicates. This fact is even more remarkable considering that silicon ranks as the second most abundant element in Earth's crust (~28%), behind oxygen at ~47%. In contrast, carbon exists in three free forms throughout the Earth in spite of comprising just a fraction of a percent of the crust.[5]

Silicon dioxide is sand, not a gas. The final reaction of carbon compounds with oxygen is carbon dioxide. In this molecule, each carbon atom forms two double bonds with two oxygen atoms. Because of the covalent nature of the double bonds, the interactions between molecules are weak. Thus, carbon dioxide exists as a gas at liquid water temperatures. Silicon atoms are larger than carbon atoms such that silicon can't form stable double bonds with oxygen. In silicon dioxide the large attraction of oxygen atoms for electrons results in a more ionic type of bond where the oxygen atoms form bridges between the silicon atoms. This bonding structure results in a crystalline solid with a high melting point. Silicon dioxide, also known as silica, is often a major part of sand and is the most abundant compound in Earth's crust.

Silicon compounds offer little "handedness." Consider your right and left hand. In an ideal world, both have the same composition and structure, but they cannot be converted from one to the other. They are mirror images, or in more technical terms, they have a definite chirality (or handedness). A large number of the compounds formed by carbon come in mirror-image copies, but that is not true for silicon compounds. Many of the important biological molecules have a definite handedness. In all life on Earth, the amino acids are left-handed, whereas the sugars are right-handed. This handedness plays a critical role in how these molecules react with other substances. For example, the one handedness of naproxen (the active ingredient in Aleve) helps relieve arthritis pain while the opposite handedness causes liver poisoning (while not relieving any pain)! From a biochemical perspective, the functioning of life seems to depend on organic molecules having a specific handedness.[6]

Silicon is relatively inactive at normal temperatures. Even though carbon and silicon can form sufficiently long molecules, carbon reacts with a wealth of other atoms in the range of temperatures where water is liquid. Carbon reacts with oxygen, hydrogen, nitrogen, phosphorus, sulfur, and a host of metals to provide the chemical diversity that life requires. In contrast, silicon reacts with a small number of elements at room temperature, although higher temperatures induce reactions with a few more elements.[7]

Silicon compounds are less abundant in the universe. As astronomers observe the heavens, they detect a large number of elements and molecules in space. A simple analysis of the molecules detected shows that carbon-based molecules vastly outnumber silicon-based ones.[8] For example, one website catalogs all the known interstellar molecules and separates them by the number of atoms the molecules include.[9] The list includes almost 200 molecules, but only 10 or so that contain silicon. Only two of those silicon molecules contain more than four atoms (C_4Si and SiH_4). Of the 60 molecules detected beyond the Milky Way Galaxy, only one contains silicon (SiO). In contrast, every one of the 60+ molecules with more than 5 atoms contains carbon. Additionally, astronomers have detected more carbon molecules with at least 5 atoms in distant galaxies (18) than silicon molecules of any size in our galaxy.

Scientists have invested great energy trying to understand the chemistry of silicon. Chemists even offer the Frederic Stanley Kipping Award "to recognize distinguished contributions to the field of silicon chemistry and, by such example, to stimulate the creativity of others."[10] The research over the past few decades shows that silicon chemistry was richer than originally expected. Even so, it appears that silicon cannot replace the complex chemistry required for life that carbon so readily offers.

Other Possible Alternatives
Discussion and investigation of alternatives to carbon-based life often occurs in the rather limited range of environments experienced on Earth's surface. This entails a certain temperature range (roughly 0°F to 200°F), pressure range (0.3 atm,[11] on top of Mount Everest, to 250 atm, at hydrothermal vents), oxygen content (none to 0.2 atm), salt concentration (0–30%) and others. Scientists who share Sagan's view suggest that our relatively small niche environment biases the conclusions we draw in assessing alternative biochemistries. While silicon shows significant deficiencies compared to carbon under Earth conditions, maybe it exhibits the chemical complexity necessary at temperatures associated with liquid nitrogen.[12]

When considering environments different from conditions on Earth, one must also look at solvents besides water and chemistries other than carbon. Pure ammonia (another cosmically abundant molecule) or ammonia/water mixtures remain liquid up to temperatures as low as -110°F at normal Earth pressures. At much higher pressures (60 atm), ammonia remains liquid in much the same temperature range as water (at normal pressure). Other proposed solvents include sulfuric acid, methane/ethane, hydrogen fluoride, and even sodium chloride or silicon dioxide. The latter two materials melt above temperatures of approximately 1,500°F and 2,900°F, respectively. Obviously, these extreme temperatures would require molecules formed from something other than carbon—maybe silicon, oxygen, or aluminum.

Such alternative solvents and backbone elements provide a fascinating arena for new research, and the diverse nature of life found on Earth gives some basis for speculating that perhaps other environments could support a completely different form of life. To explore some of the research into ways life might exist in these bizarre and extreme conditions, see the book titled *The Limits of Organic Life in Planetary Systems* published by the National Research Council.[13]

One Final Point

Have you ever hard-boiled an egg? As the egg basks in the heat of the boiling water, the gooey, gelatinous, almost-liquid egg white and the succulent yolk slowly transform into spongy and powdery solids. Yet, when the egg cools back to its original temperature, the interior remains solid. You might be inclined to think that the chemicals in the egg absorbed the heat and reacted to form different compounds, but that is not true. The same chemical compounds existed in the egg before and after boiling. So what happened?

When the chicken laid the egg, biological processes had taken the long, carbon-based molecules called proteins and folded them into a specific physical structure. Under normal biological conditions, the proteins fold inside the cell to perform specific functions. This folding depends on four things: (1) the sequencing of amino acids in the protein, which reflects the atoms in the protein and how they are bonded to each other; (2) the hydrogen bonding between different parts of the protein (see chapter 4) fold it into a secondary helical or sheet structure; (3) the helical structures then fold into a tertiary structure that allows them to; (4) combine with other proteins into a quaternary structure.[14] The final folded structure determines how the proteins behave, and all four levels of folding rely on the chemical complexity that carbon provides.

Adding a relatively small amount of energy by boiling the eggs breaks the weak bonds that allow the protein to fold, effectively uncoiling the long protein chains. The chains then clump together to form a tangled mess. Granted that mess tastes good—especially with a pinch of salt—but it is biologically useless.

The Bottom Line

Carbon's chemical complexity undergirds all (known) life on Earth in a fundamental way. Further, observations and experiments over the past few decades affirm carbon's remarkable ability to anchor life while revealing shortcomings of proposed alternative biochemistries. Even so, theoretical work shows some potential environments where truly alien life (different solvent than water, different chemistry than carbon) *might* exist. Personally, I find this research both intriguing and fascinating, and I anticipate the results from its continuation. Only by gaining a deeper understanding of how life on Earth operates, by studying how life might be different, and by searching the heavens to see what other planets reveal about the matter will we truly know whether or not life must rely on carbon. With all that said, if I were a betting man, I would still stand with Carl Sagan's sentiment that the "common chauvinism—one which, try as I might, I find I share—is carbon chauvinism."[15]

In our quest for deeper understanding, it is vital to compare our thoughts, ideas, and models against data from the real world. As we find more planets beyond the solar system, one term continually arises: habitable. Do we even know what a habitable planet looks like? What can we still learn about *this* planet that can inform searches for life on exoplanets? Our journey continues.

 Takeaways ──────────────────────────────────

- Life requires complex chemistry, including the remarkable ability of carbon to make four chemical bonds at one time.

- Carbon compounds react with oxygen to release energy that fuels biological activity, producing carbon dioxide as an essential waste product.

- Carl Sagan and others have suggested silicon as an alternative biochemistry to life, but rigorous research shows that it cannot replace the complex chemistry required for life that carbon offers.

- Other proposed solvents provide a fascinating arena for research on environments that could support a different form of life.

- Carbon's chemical complexity undergirds all known life on Earth in a fundamental way.

Chapter 7

What Does "Habitable" Mean?

Imagine using your eyes to look at a bunch of tiny, distant lights. While monitoring this scattered bunch of lights, you occasionally detect some of those lights dimming. With careful analysis of the amount of dimming, you eventually measure the physical size of the object passing in front of the light. Now here's the challenge. Using only that data, assemble a football team capable of competing in the National Football League (NFL). This seems like an impossible task, but it bears a striking resemblance to finding planets capable of hosting life.

Although scientists have discovered literally thousands of planets outside the solar system, the few dozen deemed "habitable" garner the most attention. And rightfully so, since finding planets is actually a stepping-stone to the real question: Is there life somewhere else in the universe? However, given the limited information scientists have about exoplanets, what do they mean when they define planets as "habitable"? At face value, habitable means a planet that either hosts life or could do so if life were transported there. Given the abundant capacity of Earth to host life, the term conjures images of serene meadows on expansive continents and lush islands surrounded by deep blue oceans. In a real sense, "habitable" carries everyone's experience of just how readily *Earth* supports an abundant and thriving array of life. The cold, scientific reality is that scientists currently lack the ability to detect the presence of liquid water or continents or the atmospheric composition of *any* planet with a remote chance of hosting life. So, what exactly does "habitable" mean?

Potentially Habitable (Based on Current Measurements)
As will be described in chapter 8, the list of parameters known about exoplanets typically includes the host star type, the exoplanet mass and physical size, and an assortment of properties related to the orbit (most importantly, dis-

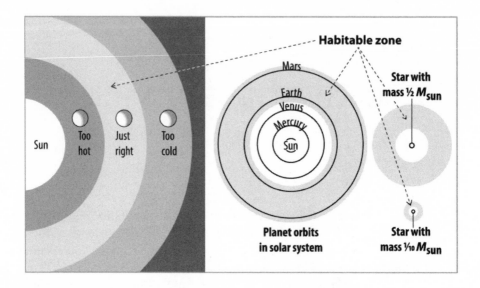

Figure 7.1: Liquid Water Habitable Zone

tance and eccentricity). Using these measured parameters, scientists then assess whether liquid water could exist on the exoplanet. To reiterate, for any exoplanet with a remote chance to host life, researchers have no way to know whether liquid water exists on the exoplanet or what gases make up its atmosphere.

Importance of Liquid Water

For decades, scientists have recognized the importance of liquid water to life as the first criterion for a habitable planet. In 1953, Harlow Shapley put forth the idea of a "liquid water belt," the idea that only planets orbiting in a specific region around a star could contain liquid water on the surface.[1] Today, scientists refer to this region as the "habitable zone" (HZ). As shown in figure 7.1, planets too close to the host star will experience runaway greenhouse heating that vaporizes all the water. Planets too far away suffer an opposite, but equally catastrophic, fate of runaway glaciation, where all the water permanently freezes into solid ice. While conceptually simple, the actual boundaries of the HZ depend on many factors such as the host star's brightness, the planet's atmospheric composition, and the reflectivity of the planet's surface.

Despite minimal information about any given exoplanet, an abundance of

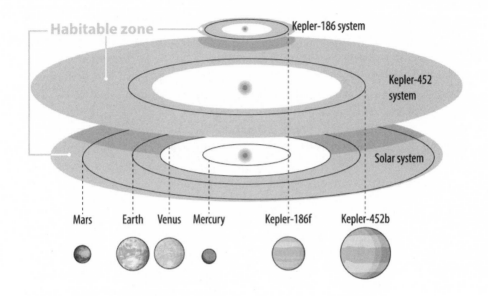

Figure 7.2: Comparison of "Habitable" Exoplanets Kepler-186f and Kepler-452b with Earth

data exists for the star it orbits. Therefore, scientists define the HZ based on the properties of the host star. Essentially, they ask the question: Given the range of reasonable planetary atmospheres and surface compositions, what are the inner and outer boundaries where an exoplanet *could* have liquid water on its surface?

Any exoplanet found orbiting inside these two boundaries for the star in question is deemed habitable. More properly, scientists deem the planet "potentially" habitable. In 2014, astronomers published the first detection of a habitable planet, Kepler-186f.[2] Because Kepler-186f orbits an M-dwarf star half the size of the Sun, the HZ resides much closer to the star when compared to Earth. A year later, astronomers' analysis of data from the Kepler mission (launched by NASA to discover Earth-size planets) revealed the detection of the first habitable planet orbiting a Sun-like star, Kepler-452b.[3]

With this definition, observations indicate that 17% of stars in the Milky Way Galaxy (MWG) host habitable planets.[4] However, one should recognize that the HZ definitions used for this calculation would also designate both Mars and Venus as habitable. Detailed studies of these two planets, via telescope and by probes at each planet, show evidence of liquid water in the past on both planets, but no definitive signs of past or present life.

One attractive aspect of defining the HZ based on observable properties relates to the prospect of future refinements. Ongoing advancements in telescope technology will bring new data to bear on the question of whether a planet actually contains liquid water. Given the broad definition of the HZ, these future advances will almost certainly reduce the number of planets declared habitable. Yet even 17% of 200 billion stars (a reasonable estimate of the number of stars in the MWG) still gives 34 billion stars with planets in the habitable zone. The unanswered question is: How far will the number drop before astronomers can determine whether exoplanets have liquid water?

A Rocky Surface

In order to have liquid water, a planet must have a solid surface and a not-too-thick atmosphere. The solar system planets fall into three classes: rocky (Mercury, Venus, Earth, and Mars), gas giants (Jupiter and Saturn), and ice giants (Uranus and Neptune). Comparing the structure of the three classes shows why only rocky planets could possibly host life.

The four rocky planets share three main internal features; namely a core, mantle, and crust. All vary markedly by planet. However, the crust on each planet provides a well-defined boundary where the body changes from solid to gas (or for Earth, solid to liquid, then to gas). Similarly, the gaseous atmosphere comprises a small fraction of the physical size of the planet. For example, Venus's atmosphere (the largest of the solar system's rocky planets) contains about 0.01% of the planet's mass. Additionally, 90% of the atmospheric mass resides within 30 km of the planet's surface. Note that the atmosphere comprises just a small fraction of the physical size of Venus since the planet's radius exceeds 6,000 km.[5]

The atmosphere of Uranus, the lightest giant planet, stands in stark contrast. With a mass between 3% and 10% of the entire planet, the atmosphere covers the outer 10,000 km of the planet's 50,000 km radius! Neptune likely has a similar structure.[6] The region below the atmosphere does contain water, ammonia, and methane, but the transition between gas-to-liquid occurs so gradually that scientists cannot delineate a clear boundary. Additionally, the enormous pressure exerted by the atmosphere means that any liquid water behaves differently from that seen on Earth's surface. For Jupiter and Saturn, the atmosphere dominates even more of the planet's size.

If dense atmospheres make a planet uninhabitable, then at somewhere between one and four times Earth's radius (the size of Uranus and Neptune), planets transition from life-stifling atmospheres to potentially life-friendly ones. One might think (or hope) this transition happens at larger values (for planet radii). After all, a larger value means more potentially habitable planets. However, small changes in a planet's radius translate into large changes in a planet's mass—mass grows as the third power of the radius or $M \propto R^3$. A planet's mass determines what type of atmosphere exists and the likelihood of a dense, life-stifling atmosphere increases rapidly as the mass increases. Research in this area shows that most planets with a measured radius (including the atmosphere) 60–75% larger than Earth's will have a dense atmosphere instead of a rocky surface where liquid water could accumulate.[7]

The situation may be even worse. Data from the Kepler telescope (validated by planetary models) indicates that rocky planets similar in mass to Earth will possess thick atmospheres composed of hydrogen (H) and helium (He). These atmospheres comprise a few percent of the exoplanet's mass. For comparison, Earth's *entire* atmosphere accounts for less than one millionth the mass of the planet. Scientists speculated that perhaps the radiation from the host star might drive the dense atmosphere away, leaving a life-friendly one. Small M-dwarf stars provide the most likely situation for such "photoevaporation"[8] because M-dwarfs emit copious amounts of UV radiation. However, these small stars give off much less light than Sun-sized stars, so planets in the habitable zone orbit much closer to the star. Thus far, models of planetary evolution show that even Earth-mass planets orbiting small M-dwarf stars retain the dense atmosphere for billions of years. This represents one more way that an Earth-mass planet in the habitable zone may actually have no chance of hosting life, or even liquid water![9]

Scientists found another process that makes finding a life-friendly atmosphere on an exoplanet orbiting an M dwarf unlikely. As described above, photoevaporation increases the energy of the molecules in an atmosphere, making the molecules more likely to escape into space. The UV and X-ray radiation emitted by M dwarfs causes another problem though. This radiation will strip the electrons off of molecules (particularly those containing oxygen and nitrogen) in an exoplanet's atmosphere. An earth-sized planet does not have enough gravitational pull to keep these electrons from flying off to space. With the loss of electrons, the remaining molecules acquire a positive charge. The charge from all the molecules causes an electric field that drives the oxygen and nitrogen containing molecules into space. Research indicates that this process will strip the exoplanet of all nitrogen and oxygen within 10 to 100 million years.[10] Even though an exoplanet around an M dwarf may have a dense atmosphere, the atmosphere will not have any nitrogen or oxygen!

Why doesn't Earth have such a dense H/He atmosphere? Roughly 100 million years after the planet formed, a large Mars-sized object collided with Earth. This collision drove away this primary atmosphere composed of H/He, allowing Earth to outgas a much thinner, secondary atmosphere composed of water vapor, carbon dioxide, sulfur dioxide, and nitrogen. Because Earth orbits a star with much less X-ray and UV radiation than an M dwarf and because it orbits at a sufficient distance, it retains the oxygen, nitrogen, and carbon dioxide of the secondary atmosphere. The collision also led to the formation of the Moon, which provides additional features that maintain Earth's habitability (see chapter 11).

A Changing Habitable Zone

When looking at a star, astronomers can determine how much radiation planets orbiting at various distances would receive. However, the amount of radiation a star emits changes over time. For example, 4 billion years ago the Sun emitted 30% less radiation than it does today. Since then, the luminosity of the Sun has steadily increased, and in another 2 billion years, it will be around 20% brighter than today. This means that the distance and width of the HZ changes over time. Since its formation, Earth has remained in the HZ and will stay there for another 2 billion years. That means it has an HZ lifetime of 6.5 billion years. Modeling of different-sized stars shows that planets between 1.2 and 2.0 astronomical units (1 AU is the distance from Earth to the Sun) can have HZ lifetimes more than 10 billion years. For stars with higher amounts of elements heavier than helium, the HZ lifetimes for Earth-like orbits extend beyond 20 billion years.[11] Many scientists see the long HZ lifetimes for planets as evidence that lots of exoplanets will have the capacity to host life.

Remember What "Habitable" Means

In the coming years, more and more headlines will announce the latest habitable planet find. Here are a few things worth remembering. First, take some time to marvel at what researchers have the ability to discover. Second, habitable refers only to the capacity to contain liquid water, although scientists have no way to actually measure its presence at this time. But, that ability will come in time. Third, don't conflate the latest declaration of a habitable planet with Earth's capacity to support life. A long string of extraordinary events has maintained Earth's habitability, but we have no reason to expect that similar events will ensure the habitability of an exoplanet. Here is an abbreviated list of those unlikely events:

1. Within 200 million years of formation, a Mars-sized body struck Earth at the just-right angle and speed to make a large moon. The size of Earth's Moon stabilizes the planet's orbit, minimizing catastrophic climate swings.[12] The Moon also generates large tides that stir the oceans and provide abundant habitats along the ocean shores. The formation of the Moon likely sped Earth's rotation to a point where a day was 4–6 hours long, resulting in horrific winds at the surface. Over the last 4.5 billion years the steady gravitational tug of the Moon slowed the rotation to the far friendlier rate seen today.

2. Between 3.8 and 4.2 billion years ago, the inner solar system experienced a barrage of comets and asteroids that pummeled surfaces of the four rocky planets. The migration of Jupiter and Saturn likely caused this bombardment and cleared out much of the debris left over from the formation of the solar system. Without this bombardment, Earth would have experienced a rate of comet and asteroid impacts roughly 1,000 times larger than measured. In other words, impacts like the one that caused the extinction of the dinosaurs would have happened every 100 *thousand* years instead of every 100 *million* years.

3. Earth started with an atmosphere devoid of free oxygen. However, anything larger than microbial life requires substantial levels of free oxygen. The addition of a permanent oxygen component to the atmosphere occurred 2.5 billion years ago as a result of increased photosynthetic activity from bacteria. This increase in oxygen appears to have caused Earth to plummet into a global glaciation that nearly covered the entire planet.[13] However, an increase in plate tectonic activity resulting from the breakup of a supercontinent released an abundance of greenhouse gases that prevented a permanent runaway icehouse condition. A similar sequence of events happened around 600–800 million years ago, accompanying a noticeable increase in the atmospheric oxygen levels. Both of these events paved the way for dramatic increases in the complexity of life on Earth.[14]

4. The Sun's output has grown steadily over the last 4.5 billion years, yet Earth's surface temperature has remained remarkably consistent. Changes in the clarity of the atmosphere (from hazy to clear with white clouds), content of the atmosphere (low O_2, high CO_2, high CH_4 to high O_2, low CO_2, low CH_4),[15] and surface cover (continents covering roughly 30% of the surface), have steadily counteracted the increasing

luminosity to maintain a habitable climate.

Astronomers continue making formidable strides toward the ability to find truly habitable planets, but it appears that the technology won't be available for another decade or two. Ultimately, scientists want the ability to detect the signatures of life on other planets—but that will require even more time. And how would we know if an exoplanet harbors life? Our odyssey continues in the next chapter.

Takeaways

- Scientists consider an exoplanet potentially habitable if it orbits between an inner and outer boundary of its host star where liquid water could exist.

- Planetary models to date show that Earth-mass planets orbiting M-dwarf stars retain dense atmospheres for billions of years, thus disqualifying them as habitable. Also Earth-mass planets orbiting M-dwarf stars experience levels of X-ray and UV radiation that drive any atmospheric oxygen and nitrogen into space.

- Habitable refers only to a planet's capacity to contain liquid water, although scientists have no way to measure its presence at this time.

- A string of extraordinary events has maintained Earth's habitability, which would be something researchers can check for on exoplanets as technology becomes available.

Chapter 8

How Would We Know If Life Exists Out There?

One of my fondest memories growing up in the Midwest was spending warm summer nights catching jars full of lightning bugs, also referred to as fireflies. For the most part, bugs carried no fascination for me, but who can resist a bug with a rear end that lights up? Of course, catching these alluring creatures did require some skill. As twilight fell, I would run through the yard with my jar in hand searching for the warm glow of the bug's light and following its silhouette in the sky. My jar, complete with the obligatory holes punched in the lid to provide the illusion of letting the bugs breathe, would soon be filled near capacity until I ultimately set the bugs loose. One night, with three lightning bugs in hand, I decided it was a good idea to release the critters in my grandparents' house. Except for the one that landed in the potato salad my mom was making, not much happened—until I went to bed that night. As I lay there in the darkness, periodic flashes of light from the remaining two bugs caught my attention.

Decades later, I can't help but recall how these little bugs help illustrate the difficulty of searching for life on planets outside our solar system. Imagine putting one of those lightning bugs on the rim of a big searchlight—the kind businesses use to attract attention as people drive across town at night. Now imagine an instrument that will, from a few miles away, be able to detect the miniscule amount of light from the lightning bug amid the flood of the searchlight. The light from a lightning bug is more than a billion times dimmer than some of the more powerful searchlights—the same difference in brightness between a planet and the star it orbits! Direct imaging of this miniscule amount of light remains the holy grail in exoplanet searches. However, scientists have developed a number of techniques that provide less information but present more manageable technical challenges.

Signs of Life

Barring an advanced civilization beaming signals at Earth, astronomers need a wealth of information to truly assess whether a planet hosts life. Aside from detecting the exoplanet, they also need to observe some sign produced *only* by life. From a naturalistic perspective, the most common form of life, if it exists beyond the confines of Earth, would be simple, single-celled organisms. From a creationist's perspective, life arises only where God creates it. This gives three different options of what scientists might find: (1) no exoplanet hosts life, (2) an exoplanet might host life and have a similar history as Earth, or (3) an exoplanet might host life that is completely different from Earth's.

Either way, the first step in the search for life entails finding evidence of liquid water. Assuming an atmosphere with enough transparency that the surface (and not the top of the clouds) reflects light back into space, the first indication of liquid water might be from measurements of the exoplanet's surface temperature. This temperature, coupled with the orbital parameters and star luminosity, tells how much greenhouse heating (see chapter 14) occurs on the planet. The amount of greenhouse heating provides knowledge about the atmospheric composition and pressure. Similarly, the albedo (reflectivity of the planet's surface), along with any variations seen, would give information about how long a day lasts, as well as what substances exist at the planet's surface. Oceans have a much lower reflectivity than freshly fallen snow, and continents often lie somewhere between these two extremes.

Perhaps the most robust sign of life relates to the gases in the exoplanet atmosphere. Because oxygen is a natural atmospheric gas on Earth, we might assume that it's abundant elsewhere in the universe—but it isn't. The highly reactive nature of free oxygen means that it quickly combines with many other compounds. The only reason Earth's atmosphere contains over 20% oxygen is because microbes produce an abundance of oxygen. Furthermore, the microbes continually replenish the oxygen used by any other organism (like humans and other large-bodied animals) or that react with surface or atmospheric materials.

Like oxygen, methane is highly reactive and requires continual replenishing to have a presence in the atmosphere. As a result, the detection of methane on Mars in recent years generated a lot of excitement about the possibility of life on the red planet.[1] As scientists investigated more closely, they found that inorganic (not involving life) processes likely produced the methane in the Martian atmosphere.[2] Clearly the difficulty of sorting out whether life processes or inorganic processes generate a signal stands as a major hurdle in assessing whether life exists on a planet. That being said, most scientists think that detection of oxygen and methane together in an exoplanet atmosphere would strongly indicate the presence of life.

Direct Imaging

Anything that scientists would consider evidence for life relies on detecting the light coming from the exoplanet. Orbits, masses, and sizes are nice but they do not provide the details necessary for detecting light. Thus, direct imaging remains the holy grail for exoplanet searches.

Astronomers use some method to block the light from the host star in order to see the much weaker (factors of a million to a billion times weaker) light signal reflected from the planet. Because the distance between a potentially habitable planet and its host star (roughly 100 million miles) pales in comparison to the distance between Earth and the host star (at least 4 light-years or 24 trillion miles), telescopes must have tremendous resolution in order to see the planet's light.

Radial Velocity Technique

On October 6, 1995, at the Cool Stars 9 conference held in Florence, Italy, Michel Mayor rocked the astronomical community by announcing the discovery of the first planet orbiting outside the solar system around a Sun-like star. Mayor and his team carefully observed the light coming from 51 Pegasi and noticed a periodic shift in the wavelengths of light it emitted. Such shifts in wavelength reveal the motion of the object in question. In other words, the size of the wavelength shifts tells us the speed, or radial velocity, of 51 Pegasi.[3] The measured speed increased and decreased just as expected if an orbiting planet were giving gravitational tugs to the star (see figure 8.1).

Instead of measuring the miniscule exoplanet light sitting in an enormous flood of light from the star, astronomers employed the radial velocity technique to search for the gravitational tugs from exoplanets. The fact that a Jupiter-sized exoplanet has one thousandth the mass of a Sun-like star makes the gravitational tugs much easier to measure.

Two earlier planets had been found orbiting a pulsar, the dead remnant of a massive star that showered anything in its vicinity with deadly radiation. The planet Mayor discovered via the radial velocity technique orbited 51 Pegasi, a star with 11% more mass than the Sun, similar metallicity and temperature to the Sun, and an age between 6 and 8 billion years. Although 51 Pegasi bore a striking resemblance to the Sun, the exoplanet Mayor found looked bizarre.

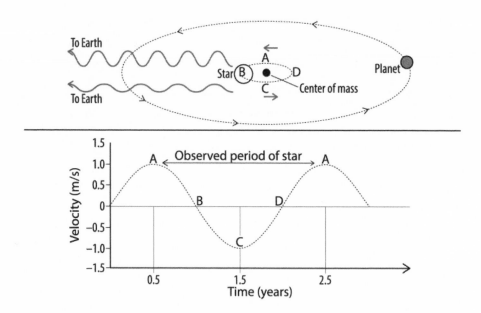

Figure 8.1: Radial Velocity Technique
Astronomers measure changes in the velocity of a host star caused by an orbiting exoplanet.

With a mass at least half that of Jupiter, the exoplanet made a complete revolution around 51 Pegasi every 4.2 days! For comparison, Jupiter takes 12 years to orbit the Sun. Even Mercury takes 88 days. Three months later (January 1996), astronomer Geoff Marcy announced the discovery of two more exoplanets, both similar in size to Jupiter. One was three times the mass of Jupiter and circled 47 Ursae Majoris (a yellow dwarf star) with a period of 3 years.[4] The other, a whopping 6.6 times the mass of Jupiter, followed a highly elongated orbit around 70 Virginis (yellow dwarf star) with a period similar to Mercury's.[5]

Strengths and Limitations
At the start of 2017, radial velocity searches had detected roughly 700 planets, with more than 100 of those residing in multi-planet systems. The sensitivity of the technique grows as the planet mass increases or as the orbit size decreases. Both conditions cause larger motions in the host star. Although this technique ushered in the age of exoplanet discoveries, it yields little information about the host planet—just the minimum mass, the orbital parameters (distance to star, eccentricity, etc.), and the age (assumed to be the same as the host star

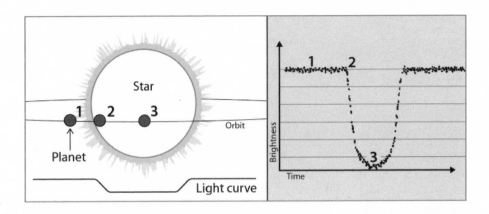

Figure 8.2: Transit Technique
Astronomers measure the dimming of a host star caused by an exoplanet passing in front of the star.

age). Because radial velocity searches look at the shift in wavelengths of light, ground-based telescopes work just as well as space-borne ones. However, current technology limits the sensitivity to planets larger than a few times the mass of Earth.

Transit Technique

In 1999, astronomers began exploiting another way to find planets outside our solar system. If the plane of a distant planetary system is aligned with Earth, then any planets might cross the disk of the star as they orbit. If so, astronomers would see a dimming of the light while the planet transits across the star (see figure 8.2). The sensitivity of this technique depends on the physical size of the star and planet. Jupiter would block out 1% of the light from the Sun since it has a diameter one-tenth as large.

While observing a star called HD 209458, Mayor and a group of astronomers saw such a dimming on September 9 and September 16.[6] Another group saw a partial transit on November 8.[7] Using this data and the extremely good measurements of the host star by the Hipparcos satellite, the scientists determined a planet with a radius 35% larger than Jupiter circled HD 209458 every 3.5 days.

In 2009, NASA launched the Kepler spacecraft to monitor 145,000 stars for signs of exoplanet transits. With a planned lifetime of 4 years, the observatory

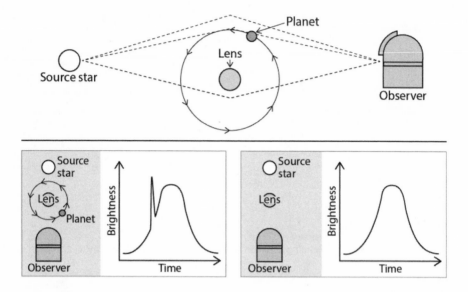

Figure 8.3: Gravitational Microlensing Technique
Astronomers measure the brightness of a background star increase as a foreground star/planet bends more light toward an observer on Earth.

had the sensitivity to find Earth-sized planets in Earth-like orbits around Sun-like stars. The mission suffered various technical problems in 2012 and 2013, but it still discovered over 2,000 exoplanets. A dozen of these planets are similar in size to Earth and orbit in the habitable zone with the potential to host liquid water!

Strengths and Limitations
Using just the transit technique, astronomers can determine the physical size of an exoplanet as well as its orbital parameters. Current technology allows astronomers to find planets as small or smaller than Earth in Earth-like orbits. Earth would block one ten-thousandth the light from the Sun, so only telescopes in space achieve this sensitivity. Moreover, because the transit technique relies on the proper alignment of the Earth, exoplanet, and star, astronomers can find only a small fraction of the exoplanets that might exist. (Radial velocity searches often add the mass of the planet.) Occasionally, astronomers get information from the exoplanet's atmosphere as the transit begins and ends.

But so far, only Jupiter-like planets have yielded this atmospheric information.

Microlensing Technique

According to Einstein's theory of general relativity, any massive body warps the fabric of space in its vicinity. This fact provides astronomers with another way to find planets around distant stars. If a planet-hosting star crosses the line of sight between Earth and a more distant star, the gravitational warping of space around the planet and closer star acts like a lens. This lens will amplify the light from the more distant star as it passes by both the planet and the closer star. The closer the passage to the line of sight, the greater the magnification (see figure 8.3). By analyzing the amount of magnification and the length of time that the magnification lasts, astronomers can determine the orbital parameters of the planet and its mass. The first exoplanet detected via microlensing goes by the name OGLE 2003-BLG-235L b.[8] Both the orbit and mass of this exoplanet look strikingly similar to Jupiter's.

Strengths and Limitations

As of 2017, astronomers have discovered just over 50 exoplanets via microlensing. This technique offers two advantages in the search for Earth-like planets. First, planets with masses smaller than Earth's cause light amplifications large enough to be seen with current telescope technologies. The same is true even for planets with orbits larger than Jupiter's. Second, astronomers can find exoplanets over a much larger fraction of the galaxy compared to other techniques. Transit and radial velocity surveys typically find exoplanets around stars that are hundreds of light-years away. Microlensing routinely finds exoplanets around stars thousands of light-years away. However, as with the radial velocity technique, microlensing provides only the mass and orbital parameters of the exoplanet. Additionally, the technique relies on random alignments of the lensing system with more distant stars. This means that astronomers get only one chance to detect the exoplanet and have no opportunity to take follow-up observations to measure more details in the future.

Direct Imaging Technique

As mentioned earlier, direct imaging provides the only way to determine if life exists on an exoplanet. Variations in the amount of light received from the exoplanet give key insights about the structure of the exoplanet's surface. The distribution of light at different wavelengths provides important data about the composition of the exoplanet's atmosphere. But directly detecting light from

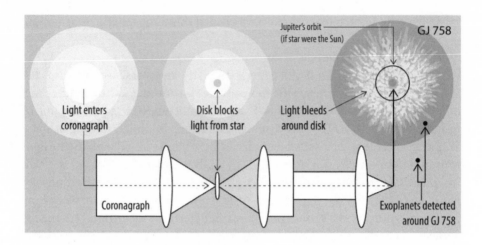

Figure 8.4: Direct Imaging Technique
Using a coronagraph to block light from the star, the Subaru telescope detected one (and maybe two) exoplanets around GJ 758.

an exoplanet is not easy. The first step involves blocking the light from the star in order to see the light from the planet.

Astronomers employ two different methods to block the starlight, using either an interferometer or a coronagraph. The more useful coronagraph technique is basically a sophisticated version of putting your hand in front of a light to see better at night. As the light enters the telescope, lenses focus the light into an image. Where the image forms, the telescope has a barrier that prevents the starlight from passing. The remaining light travels through sophisticated optical devices to make an image of everything else but the starlight.

Astronomers used direct imaging to find two notable exoplanets orbiting Kepler-70. Kepler-70 b and c both have masses roughly half that of Earth and radii similar to Earth, plus they orbit the star with periods of a few hours! Kepler-70 is a post red-giant star, meaning it has exhausted all its hydrogen fuel, swelled to enormous size, and then collapsed to a radius about 20% that of the Sun as it started fusing helium in its core (see chapter 12). As Kepler-70 swelled, it likely engulfed the two exoplanets, dragging them closer to the star from more distant orbits. It appears that these two exoplanets were once gas giants whose atmospheres evaporated under the intense heat inside Kepler-70.[9] That would mean that Kepler-70 b and c consist of just the cores, similar to the ones that originally accumulated copious amounts of gas to form Jupiter and Saturn. Thus, further studies of the composition and nature of Kepler 70 b and c will help astronomers better understand the process of planet formation.

Strengths and Limitations
The main strength of direct imaging compared to all other techniques is the ability to measure light from the exoplanet itself. Coronagraphs do an impressive job of blocking light from the central star, but they have limitations. Even with careful designing of the optics, some light from the central star gets around the obstacles and bleeds into the region where exoplanets reside. Because the star is so much brighter, it does not take much bleed-through to wash out the signal from the dimmer exoplanet. Almost all of the 70 or so exoplanets detected via direct imaging have masses much larger than Jupiter and orbit at great distances from their host stars. This makes sense because larger planets reflect (or emit) more light and their greater distances from the star make it easier to find the exoplanet's light amid the starlight. While other techniques provide relatively sensitive measurements of the exoplanet mass, direct imaging gives only loose constraints based on the star's age and the exoplanet's temperature.

It bears mentioning that scientists continue to develop more-sensitive telescopes that will eventually image Earth-sized planets. Although current coronagraphs see only exoplanets much larger than Jupiter, new coronagraphs operating in space will have sensitivity to image Jupiter-sized planets (WFIRST [Wide Field Infrared Survey Telescope] is slated for launch in 2025) and even Earth-sized planets (either HabEx [Habitable Exoplanet Imaging Mission] or LUVOIR [Large UV/Optical/Infrared Surveyor] will be recommended by the 2020 Decadal Survey). Additionally, the "starshade" technique of blocking light from the star before it reaches the telescope may permit imaging of Earth-sized exoplanets around nearby stars.[10]

When Will We Know?
Scientists continue to search for exoplanets and have found thousands by using these tools. They push the technology to even greater sensitivity. In parallel with the effort to improve telescopes, scientists are also trying to better understand what signatures life might leave that they can detect. On Earth, life produces large methane (CH_4), oxygen (O_2), and nitrous oxide (N_2O) signatures in the atmosphere. However, life produces a host of other molecules in much smaller quantities. Perhaps life on other planets might generate larger quantities of some other gas. Consequently, scientists are compiling lists of all

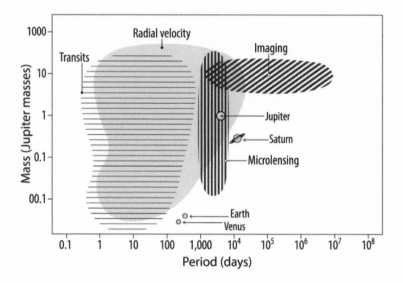

Figure 8.5: Exoplanet Masses vs. Orbital Periods
As seen by the solar system planets labeled on the plot, our current telescope technology would not yet be capable of detecting our solar system planets if they were orbiting another star. Note the logarithmic scales on both axes.

possible molecules and then asking which ones might life generate to detectable quantities in an exoplanet atmosphere.[11]

As shown in figure 8.5, even with the great strides made over the last two decades, our current technology would be unable to detect the solar system planets if they were orbiting another star. The James Webb Space Telescope, Hubble's successor, is scheduled for launch in 2018 and will dramatically improve our ability to study the heavens. It will improve upon Hubble's abilities to detect atmospheric gases during exoplanet transits and have some ability to search for exoplanets via direct imaging. However, except for some fortuitous circumstances, it will not have the ability to detect the signatures of life from Earth-like planets. None of the currently scheduled missions can. Even if many of the proposed missions are launched, it will be a couple of decades before we can truly assess whether any distant planet actually hosts life.

In the early 1990s, only 8 planets were known. Less than 30 years later, that small catalog has grown to several thousand. Equally important, astronomers have filled their workbenches with an incredible suite of tools to find and study exoplanets. Just imagine what they will accomplish in the next three decades! Nevertheless, scientists are nowhere close to discovering life of any kind outside Earth. What will it take? Decades and decades? In the meantime, are there other types of alien life and alien worlds to consider? Yes, there are.

 Takeaways

- Most scientists think that the detection of oxygen and methane together in an exoplanet atmosphere would strongly indicate the presence of life.

- In the search for exoplanets, scientists have employed direct imaging, the radial velocity technique, the transit technique, and the microlensing technique, all with strengths and limitations; no planet to date shows signs of hosting life.

- Even if scheduled missions are launched, it will be decades before scientists can truly assess whether any exoplanet can support life.

Chapter 9

Does a Multiverse Exist?

If the Sun quit shining right now, we would not know for more than eight minutes. It takes light (or any other form of information) that long to travel from the Sun to Earth. Light covers the distance from the Moon in about a second. Light from Andromeda, the closest large galaxy, travels for 2.5 million years before reaching Earth. The more distant the object, the longer light must travel. Since the universe is only 14 billion years old, this principle means that astronomers can define a boundary containing all the observable stuff of the universe. Beyond that boundary, the universe is not old enough for light to traverse the distance to Earth. By any human measure, that boundary is an incredible distance away, but it does mean that our observable universe has a definite size, which raises an interesting question: What, if anything, exists outside the observable universe?

Anything existing outside our observable universe would reside in a separate universe, thus defining a *multiverse*.[1] Now, you might object that this definition seems arbitrary since the simplest assumption of what might exist beyond the boundary is a whole lot more of the same stuff seen in the observable universe. However, this definition brings one major benefit: It quantifies the universe in a defensible way while providing direction for scientific investigation of anything that might exist beyond the universe.

Evidence for a Multiverse: Problems with the Big Bang

To understand why scientists think a multiverse exists requires a general understanding of big bang cosmology. During the earliest moments, the universe experienced unimaginably hot temperatures (so extreme that the surface of the Sun would seem cool by comparison), incredible densities, and remarkable uniformity. As the universe transitioned from this initial state to one filled with galaxies, stars, and planets, the following three important changes occurred.

The Cosmic Microwave Background Radiation
Around 400,000 years after the big bang, the universe cooled to 3000°C, at essentially the same time everywhere in the universe. Below this temperature, electrons can combine with protons to form neutral hydrogen atoms.[2] Thus, the light emitted from the formation of the neutral hydrogen atoms records the time when the temperature of the universe dropped below 3000°C. The ensuing expansion of the universe during the last 14 billion years has stretched that light so that scientists detect it now as microwaves. The uniformity of this cosmic microwave background (CMB) radiation provides strong evidence that we live in a big bang universe.

However, the uniformity does pose a problem. Calculating the expansion of the universe as far back as possible, scientists have determined that the region that emits the CMB we see in one direction would never be in contact with the region emitting the CMB from the opposite direction. Consequently, there is no reason for those two regions to have the same temperature, but they do. Additionally, although many measurements confirm the uniformity of the CMB, scientists have measured tiny ripples in the CMB that result in galaxies, stars, and planets forming. *Standard* big bang cosmology has no explanation for these two facts.

Magnetic Monopoles
In the first fraction of a second (less than a trillionth of a trillionth of a second), the universe cooled enough for some monumental changes. Though an incredibly brief period of time, this moment shaped the future of the universe. The temperature dropped such that the strong nuclear interaction separated from the weak nuclear and electromagnetic interactions. This transition laid the foundation for the amount of normal and dark matter the universe would contain. The amount of dark energy was determined even earlier.

One interesting consequence of this transition concerns the production of magnetic monopoles (in lay terms, a north pole without a south pole). Electric charge comes in monopole form: An electron is an electric monopole with negative charge and a positron is an electric monopole with positive charge. Magnets exist only in dipole form: Every north pole is paired with a south pole. Theoretical modeling shows that the separation of the strong nuclear and electroweak interactions produces an abundance of magnetic monopoles, but scientists find no evidence that they exist. Standard big bang cosmology has no explanation for this discrepancy.

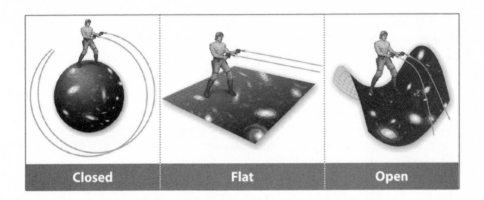

Figure 9.1: Geometry of the Universe
In a closed geometry, parallel lines converge whereas they diverge in an open geometry. In a flat geometry, parallel lines stay the same distance apart.

A Flat Geometry

The universe has expanded continuously over the last 14 billion years. The incredible amount of mass in the universe should cause the expansion to slow down. If the universe contained enough mass, the expansion would eventually stop and switch to contraction. With too little mass, the expansion would continue forever. With the just-right amount of mass, the expansion would gradually slow down and eventually stop (although it would take forever to do so). In scientific terms, the three scenarios correspond to closed, open, or flat geometries for the universe. If the universe were two-dimensional, these geometries would look like the surface of a ball, the surface of a saddle, or a piece of paper (see figure 9.1). Even without understanding dark matter or discovering dark energy, scientists knew that the geometry of the universe was uncomfortably close to flat. A universe that supports life must be close to flat,[3] but flat is unstable. If the early universe were slightly open or slightly closed, it would be nowhere near flat today. Based on scientists' calculations, in order for the universe to appear flat today, the mass density needed to vary by no more than one part in 10^{24} (although some calculations put the number at one part in 10^{60})![4] Again, standard big bang cosmology offers no explanation for this incredible degree of fine-tuning.

Inflation to the Rescue

In the 1970s and 80s, many scientists were working to resolve these problems with big bang cosmology. One group working on the magnetic monopole problem recognized that a specific kind of "phase transition" in the early universe could suppress the number of magnetic monopoles produced in the observable universe. Detailed studies of this phase transition showed that it also caused the universe to rapidly expand (exponentially, not linearly) in a way that solved the fine-tuning of the universe's geometry and naturally produced the uniformity of the CMB. Additionally, the exponential expansion amplified subtle quantum fluctuations to reproduce the tiny temperature ripples found in the CMB.[5]

Adding inflation, the moniker given to the period of rapid expansion, solved three large problems associated with standard big bang models. This fact convinced many scientists of inflation's validity, and ongoing observations of the CMB and the clustering of galaxies in the universe continue to buttress the model. So how does inflation relate to the multiverse? It does so in two ways.

First, the exponential expansion of the universe means that our observable universe comprises just a small fraction of the amount of stuff that exists. As scientists calculate the size of this multiverse, they get numbers ranging from one thousand times the size of the observable universe to something that is spatially infinite. If inflation happened, a multiverse exists. While this type of multiverse is noncontroversial (in my opinion), all it really says is that a lot more of the same stuff exists beyond what scientists can measure.

Second, scientists have sought diligently to understand the mechanism behind inflation. One early issue with inflationary big bang cosmology was called the graceful exit problem. Scientists know of mechanisms to drive inflation, but it must end in a rather delicate way to explain the smoothness of the CMB. All forms of inflation posit some field that fills space. The important detail of this field relevant to inflation is that the value of the field starts at something other than its lowest state. Space with this field in an excited state will exponentially expand. When the field decays to the ground state, the rapid exponential expansion will cease and a much slower expansion will ensue. Any workable model of inflation must produce the uniformity measured in the cosmic background radiation. Investigating the details of how inflation would end never gave the graceful exit required to match the CMB, until physicist Alan Guth provided an insightful solution.[6]

Prior to Guth's idea, the common picture of inflation went something like this:

- Space-time was created at the start of the big bang.

- The universe expanded, undergoing a period of inflationary expansion in the first fraction of a second. During this inflationary epoch, the universe expanded by an enormous factor (doubling in size between 25 and 100 times) in less than 10^{-34} seconds.
- The inflation field decayed (throughout the observable universe) to give the expansion seen today.
- The universe cooled down, eventually emitting the CMB and forming stars and galaxies. Almost 14 billion years later, human beings arrived on planet Earth.

All scenarios following this progression suffer from the graceful exit problem and cannot be reconciled with the CMB measurements. Guth's solution proceeds along this line:

- Some preexisting "space" continually undergoes inflation.
- The inflation potential decayed in some particular region of this "überspace," signifying the start of our universe.
- If viewed from outside our universe, this bubble-region where inflation ceased would grow larger as time progresses. The boundary between the inflating region outside the bubble and the noninflating region inside the bubble represents the big bang. Regions inside the bubble cannot see out; regions outside the bubble cannot see in.
- The region inside the bubble cooled down, eventually emitting the CMB radiation and forming stars and galaxies. Almost 14 billion years later, human beings arrived on planet Earth.

The only theoretical models of inflation that reproduce the CMB posit a scenario like the latter sequence. If these mechanisms are correct (and that's still a big *if*), then a multiverse certainly exists. This type of multiverse contains other bubbles where the physical laws may appear very differently than in our universe. The strengths of the fundamental interactions (strong and weak nuclear, electromagnetic, and gravity), as well as the physical constants like the speed of light and the charge of an electron, could be different.

From a scientific perspective, the idea of a multiverse is reasonable. Still, a number of misunderstandings surround the concept. For one, *scientists did not invent the multiverse simply to get around the abundant evidence that our universe appears fine-tuned to support life.* It's true that acceptance of the multiverse often corresponds with a belief that it solves the fine-tuning problems. Multiverse ideas have existed for at least the last hundred years. However, they gained a larger acceptance only with the development of cosmological models that both predict the existence of a multiverse *and* provide good explanations of the universe in which we live.

On the other hand, there are some who argue that the multiverse solves a wealth of fine-tuning problems and then use that as evidence for the multiverse. This line of reasoning seems circular to me.

The Bottom Line

Good scientific evidence makes the existence of a multiverse a reasonable conclusion (although not a sure thing). The real issue surrounding the multiverse (as defined in this chapter) is whether it fits more comfortably within a theistic worldview or a strictly naturalistic worldview. The existence of a multiverse does raise some vexing questions regarding the search for life beyond Earth (see chapter 17). At the end of the day, one can make a strong case that the theistic worldview provides the best explanation of all the issues raised by the existence of a multiverse (see chapter 10).

Affirming the existence of a multiverse is one thing, but use it to explain all the incremental, fine-tuned steps leading to life in the cosmos, is another. Does the multiverse account for all the improbable events on Earth or on any other exoplanet?

 Takeaways ——————————————————————————

- Inflationary theory has emerged to help explain anomalies in big bang cosmology, including measurements in the cosmic microwave background radiation, magnetic monopoles, and the universe's flat geometry.

- In recent decades, inflation as a model for the universe's expansion has explained the discrepancies with reasonable satisfaction, but it also points to a multiverse.

- Physicist Alan Guth has provided a multiverse solution to the graceful exit problem that can be reconciled with CMB measurements and inflation.

- If true, then a multiverse certainly exists, but it is essential to remember that scientists did not invent the multiverse to get around the idea that evidence seems to support a fine-tuned, life-hospitable universe.

Chapter 10

Does a Multiverse Solve
All These Problems?

A few years ago out of sheer curiosity, I searched Google for an explanation of the multiverse. One of my favorite results showed a picture of a father and daughter reading a bedtime story. The daughter asks the father, "Daddy, what's a multiverse?" The dad replies, "It's a plot device for lazy writers."

Bad jokes aside, from a scientific perspective, solid evidence supports the claim that a multiverse exists (see chapter 9). Assuming for now that this evidence withstands further testing, a more important question comes to mind: Does a multiverse explain the improbable string of events necessary for life on Earth?

Radically Changing the Question

In a single universe, scientists must explain how the universe starts, then how it progresses from a sea of subatomic particles to a place where Earth exists. The description must answer questions like:

- Why do the laws of physics permit the formation of life's building blocks (carbon, oxygen, hydrogen, etc., as well as planets and stars)?
- How do all those building blocks form?
- What steps transpired in Earth's transformation from a dark, hostile-to-life water world to one hosting a thriving and diverse array of life?

Scientific investigations of these questions over the last century repeatedly demonstrate that many of the requirements for life seem to hinge on extremely unlikely or finely tuned events. Small changes in the strengths of the fundamental forces result in a universe with no carbon, oxygen, or hydrogen (see chapter 15). A planet of the wrong size or orbiting the wrong kind of star would lose its water too quickly (see chapters 5 and 7).

For a single universe, the relevant question is, how did all of these seemingly improbable events transpire to produce the origin and history of life on Earth? Assuming that life is purely physical (that life simply results from the proper arrangement of atoms), the multiverse changes the nature of the question. The Bible describes a nonphysical nature to humanity; that is, we are the union of spiritual and physical components. Consequently, assembling all the atoms of my body in the proper configuration somewhere else would still not produce another Jeff Zweerink. However, anyone arguing for naturalism is stuck with the notion that the physical realm is all that exists.

Although the events leading to life may seem rare or unusual, in the multiverse every possible thing happens somewhere. In fact, *every possible thing happens many times*. This means that scientists must consider the possibility that multiple copies of our observable universe exist or that we may be one giant Boltzmann brain or even that we may exist inside some vast computer simulation run by a super-advanced civilization (see chapter 17). Thus the question changes from "How do we explain how unlikely life appears?" to "How typical are we compared to all the different forms of life that exist?"

What If We Are Boltzmann Brains?

Many of the most straightforward ways of comparing the number of "ordinary observers" (OOs) with the number of "Boltzmann brains" (BBs, see pages 148–149) leads to the conclusion that BBs vastly outnumber OOs. However, one must use caution because these counting exercises usually involve comparing different infinite numbers, and such comparisons are difficult at best. With that caveat, it's far more likely that we are BBs instead of OOs. Therefore, the typical explanation for the history of life on Earth is nothing but a nice story with no correspondence to reality.

Consider the implications of our existence as a BB. The simplest and most abundant type of BB is a minimum-sized thermal fluctuation that results in a brain briefly popping into existence, recognizing it exists, and fluctuating out of existence just as quickly. This type of BB would exist for a fraction of a second and observe a very disordered universe. The probability of such an event starts incredibly small and becomes even more remote as the duration of the BB increases and as the orderliness of the observed universe increases. In other words, if we are BBs, we are an incredibly rare form of BB since we see an incredibly well-ordered universe that has existed for a long duration. Our appearance as an improbable, atypical BB would provide an argument that we were here for a purpose and not as a random event.

Although all this discussion about life arising by thermal fluctuations can cause one's brain to hurt (pun intended), it also highlights a few apologetic points. Some scientists don't like such a conclusion, so they look for solutions. In my assessment, the solutions they adopt to solve the BB problem still buttress fine-tuning arguments for God's existence.

The first solution argues that a universe that decays on a timescale similar to its current age would remove any consideration of BBs. One example of this approach recognizes that the mass of the Higgs boson[1] and the top quark (an elementary particle) impact the stability of the vacuum in our universe. The measurements of these two masses (top quark at 173 GeV/c^2 and the Higgs boson at 126 GeV/c^2) imply that our universe resides in a low-energy state but not *the* lowest-energy state. That opens the possibility that our universe could tunnel to the lowest-energy state with catastrophic consequences. The mass of the top quark and Higgs boson must be finely tuned so that this decay happens late enough for the universe to support humanity, but not so late that the Boltzmann brain problem arises.[2]

The second solution to avoid the BB problem imposes constraints on how to regulate the infinities involved in counting comparisons. Basically, scientists must impose some condition such that counting the possible outcomes results in finite numbers.[3] Two scientists evaluated a mechanism to regulate infinities in such a way that the universe still exhibits an arrow of time (or causality). They did find some conditions that limited BB formation while preserving an arrow of time.[4] This work mirrors other research into the early moments of the universe by recognizing that an arrow of time represents a fundamental requirement for a habitable universe.[5]

Maybe the reason sci-fi shows usually don't encounter BB aliens (for one notabable exception, see the whale in *The Hitchhiker's Guide to the Galaxy*) flows from the recognition that a BB-dominated universe is cognitively unstable.[6] In a BB-dominated universe, the best explanation for our existence is that we're BBs. (One other option is to fine-tune the multiverse so as not to produce BBs.) However, if we are BBs, then there is no reason to trust our thoughts about the universe because they simply reflect the fluctuation that produced us. Of course, none of this matters if humans are not simply an arrangement of atoms but instead the union of a body and soul as described in the Bible.

What If We Are Simulations?

I spent many years looking for gamma rays from exploded stars and distant galaxies. Part of the process for detecting these energetic messengers (the gamma rays in question carried up to a billion times more energy than the

X-rays used by doctors) included simulating the gamma ray as it interacted with the atmosphere and the resulting light as it propagated through the telescope. One thing I can say for sure—I simulated far more gamma rays than I ever detected. If advanced civilizations exist, then it may be far more likely that we live in one of their simulations. This assumes that the civilization has sufficient resources and that some mechanism exists to run such a simulation. More importantly, it presumes that properly applied physics and/or computer algorithms can produce consciousness! But for a moment, let's pretend that all these conditions can be met.

Interestingly, the picture painted by the Bible shares much with the idea that we are a "simulation." For instance, one reason God created this universe is to provide an arena for the conquest of good over evil. Upon completing that conquest, God will replace this universe (according to this view) with a more permanent creation where humans will each enjoy an intimate relationship with him—which is the ultimate reality.

However, unlike simulations where everything ceases to exist, God will transport us into the new "simulation" where wonders beyond our imagination await. Further, death, decay, and pain no longer exist because the old "simulation" will have passed away.

What If a Bunch of Us Exist?

Concepts like identity, free will, and justice play a fundamental role in how humanity thinks—especially in the West. The existence of other regions (the multiverse) would dramatically impact how we think about these important concepts: "Am I really being held accountable for my actions when I don't commit those actions in some other regions of space or when I am not punished for them in others? Is that person in the other region really me?" These are some of the interesting and alarming questions of a spatially infinite (or sufficiently large) level I (one) multiverse that need addressing.

Some have argued that these other copies of universes, while interesting, have no bearing on what happens here. However, if everything that happens simply results from a specific arrangement of atoms, how can anything like free will, justice, and even identity be relevant?

One Universal (Or Should It Be Multiversal?) Solution

All these other possibilities rely on life, specifically human life, resulting from the proper arrangement of atoms. What if humanity is more than mere material, and we have some immaterial soul? No amount of rearranging the stuff of the universe would ever produce human life—regardless of how large the multiverse is! The Bible describes humanity as being made in God's image (Genesis 1:26–27). Specifically, each human is the union of a spirit (or soul) and a body. As such, we exist and function in this universe but have the capacity to relate to God. If Scripture gives an accurate description of human existence, then all the odd problems of weird life in the multiverse are solved!

Multiverse theories can address the fine-tuned appearance of our observable universe and the events that make advanced life possible, but they still raise more complicated questions than they answer. Do multiple copies of me making slightly different choices exist? Do random processes spontaneously pop sentient beings briefly into existence? Are we just part of a highly complex, but nonetheless unreal, simulation? The list of challenges grows.

These last two chapters covered necessary ground in our exoplanet search for life out there, but the reading may have been tough on the brain. Other important questions frequently arise, as you may have seen from the table of contents. A certain planet was demoted from its status as such in the solar system. Why is that significant in the search for extraterrestrial life?

 Takeaways ─────────────────────────

- In the multiverse, every possible thing happens somewhere many times; thus, multiple copies of our universe may exist.

- Two solutions presented for the Boltzmann brain (multiverse) problem still buttress fine-tuning arguments for God's existence.

- The idea of a "simulation" of sorts finds resonance with the Bible, in that this universe is temporary; Christians look forward to a new creation without sin and evil in the presence of God forever.

- If the Bible is correct, then concepts like free will, justice, and identity make sense in the multiverse.

Chapter 11

Why Isn't Pluto a Planet?

On October 21, 2003, astronomical images taken at Palomar Observatory set in motion a sequence of events leading to a momentous decision.[1] A team of astronomers was searching for more objects orbiting in the distant reaches of the solar system. Software scanned a few images taken over a few hours looking for anything that moved during that time. Finding nothing of interest, astronomers set the images aside to gather dust in the proverbial drawer for over a year. Upon closer inspection by eye (instead of computer), the team made a groundbreaking decision. On July 29, 2005, they announced the discovery of 2003 UB313, an object orbiting beyond Neptune but brighter than Pluto. Thirteen months later, scientists made the shocking announcement— Pluto was no longer a planet![2]

More importantly, the classification developed by the International Astronomical Union (IAU) will make future discoveries of objects inside and outside our solar system easier to catalog as planets or something else.

So, why exactly is Pluto no longer deemed worthy of planet status? And why does it matter in our search for a life-friendly exoplanet?

What Makes a Planet?
To understand the criteria used in the IAU definition of a planet requires some knowledge of how planetary systems form. The first step involves something that triggers a large cloud of gas and dust to start collapsing. As the cloud collapses, it will form a dense inner region (the eventual star) with a disk of material rotating around it. The dust and ice particles in the disk will begin to stick together as they collide. These clumps of dust and ice eventually grow large enough to gravitationally attract other disk material until they reach diameters about the size of football fields. The football field-sized bodies continue growing by colliding with one another over the next few million years. After 5–10

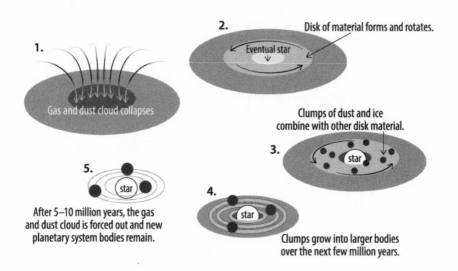

Figure 11.1: Major Stages of Planetary Formation

million years, the star will generate enough radiation to blow all the remaining gas and dust out of the planetary system.

For the objects growing outside the snow line (the distance from the Sun where temperatures were sufficiently low for abundant ice particles to form, roughly 5 AU), this process proceeded quickly enough so that the resulting bodies could rapidly collect the gas remaining in the cloud. This led to the formation of the solar system's gas giants (Jupiter, Saturn, Uranus, and Neptune). Inside the snow line, the lack of ices meant that 50–100 Moon-to-Mars-sized objects, called planetesimals, formed. Over the next hundred million years, these objects collided to form the four terrestrial planets (Mercury, Venus, Earth, and Mars). The final collision for each of these planets dramatically affected their futures (more on that later).

The above scenario represents the most commonly accepted core-accretion model of planetary formation. It tends to work well for terrestrial-sized planets, while a core-collapse model generates gas giants more effectively. For purposes of defining planets, however, the differences between the two models are irrelevant.

Given this basic understanding of planetary formation, the IAU decided on three characteristics that all planets must meet. First, the object must orbit around the Sun (or a star when discussing exoplanets). Thus, Europa, Titan, and other moons (larger than Pluto) in the solar system fail to achieve planethood because they orbit one of the gas giants. Second, the body must have sufficient mass that its self-gravity overcomes all the rigid body forces such that it assumes an essentially spherical shape. This criterion eliminates the vast majority of asteroids and comets. Third, the object must clear out the neighborhood around its orbit. Pluto clearly meets the first two criteria, but it fails the third—like all the other known objects beyond the orbit of Neptune. Consequently, Pluto, Eris (formerly known as 2003 UB313), Sedna, and many other objects are known as dwarf planets rather than planets.

Though the question of Pluto's "planethood" still troubles many (a public forum at Harvard University voted that Pluto should still be a planet[3]), from a scientific and educational perspective, the decision was justified. Scientists already know of a dozen objects in the solar system similar in size and orbit to Pluto and expect to find another couple hundred more as they develop the technology to explore the outer solar system. If Pluto were reinstated as a planet, then it would be expected that these new objects would also be classified as planets. Consider the challenge of students having to memorize tens or hundreds of names in order to know all the planets in the solar system! More importantly, future discoveries of objects inside and outside our solar system will more definitively fit into the IAU's classification system.

The topic of planetary formation and the question of Pluto's planetary status raise some interesting points concerning Earth's capacity to support life. Let's look at some of those issues in more detail.

One Final Step Clears the Way

The discovery of exoplanets made scientists reassess the final phases of planetary formation. In our solar system, the terrestrial planets orbit closer to the Sun and the gas giants farther out. This arrangement arises because the ices necessary for rapid planetary growth (required by the gas giants) form only outside a certain distance from the Sun, called the frost or snow line. Inside that distance, the Sun provides enough radiation to prevent ice formation. Currently, the distance to the snow line is around 5 AU (one AU is the distance from the Earth to the Sun). However, the presence of gas and debris in the early solar system as well as the reduced output of the Sun brought the snow line into a distance of 2.7 AU—roughly the distance of the asteroid belt.

In 1995, astronomers discovered 51 Pegasi b, the first exoplanet orbiting a Sun-like star. Aside from the historical nature of the discovery, the exoplanet's characteristics caused quite a stir. With a mass at least half of Jupiter's,

Changes in Solar System as Gas Giants Migrate

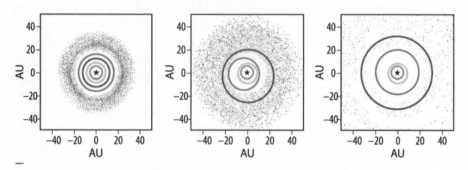

Figure 11.2: Gas Giant Migration Effects in the Solar System
As time progresses from left to right, the orbits of the gas giants spread out, clearing the solar system of debris and causing Neptune and Uranus to change positions.

51 Pegasi b is clearly a gas giant. However, it orbits the host star with a period of four days at a distance of 0.053 AU! Finding such a massive planet so close to its star made astronomers realize that planets can actually move from the location where they form. The discovery of hundreds of these "hot Jupiters" means that any realistic model must include planetary migration. So how did migration affect the solar system?

The most accepted model for the formation of the solar system, the so-called Nice (pronounced "niece") model, starts with the gas giants forming in more tightly packed orbits (5.5–17 AU) than they currently occupy (5–30 AU). A large disk of ice and rock planetesimals (roughly 35 times Earth's mass) orbited in the region from 17 to 35 AU. Gravitational encounters of the most distant gas giant would scatter these planetesimals inward while the gas giant moved outward. The inward moving planetesimals would then interact with the next gas giant until they encounter Jupiter. The enormous gravitational influence of Jupiter scatters the planetesimals into highly elliptical orbits or even ejects them from the solar system, causing Jupiter to migrate closer to the Sun. The net effect of this model results in (1) the clearing of 99% of the planetesimal disk mass; (2) a *small* inward migration of Jupiter to its current orbit; (3) outward migration of Saturn, Neptune, and Uranus to their current orbits; (4) Uranus and Neptune swapping orbits; and (5) maybe the ejection of a hypothetical fifth gas giant.

The first and second effects figure prominently in Earth's capacity to support life. Because the migration in the Nice model clears so much mass from the solar system, the rate of asteroids and comets hitting Earth drops by roughly a factor of 1,000. Consider the consequences of an impact rate this much larger.

As will be discussed in chapter 12, a six-mile wide object slammed into the Earth near the Yucatán Peninsula 66 million years ago. The impact ejected debris, which rained back onto Earth, and the ensuing climate change wiped three-fourths of all animal life, including the dinosaurs, from the planet. Scientists estimate that such impacts currently happen every 50–100 million years. Had the migration of the giant planets not reduced this rate by a factor of 1,000, these events would happen every 50–100 thousand years. In other words, since humanity arrived on Earth roughly 100,000 to 150,000 years ago, one would expect two or three of these extinction-level impacts just within that timescale. Given that it seems to take something on the order of one million years to recover from one of these extinction events, an impact rate 1,000 times higher would dramatically affect Earth's capacity to support life!

If Jupiter had migrated to a location inside Mercury's orbit (like the hot Jupiter exoplanets observed), it would have dramatic consequences on the location and formation of the terrestrial planets. Even the small migration of Jupiter toward the Sun caused significant disruption on the other large gas giants. As Jupiter moves through the inner part of the solar system, it would likely eject any planets that had already formed (leaving the solar system with no Earth), or it would disrupt the formation of the terrestrial planets. Some astronomers speculate that planets may be able to form after Jupiter migrates through, but, as of yet, no hard evidence supports this notion.

Making the Moon

The Moon plays an important role in Earth's capacity to maintain oceans of liquid water.[4] It minimizes the wobbling of Earth's rotation axis. It causes tides that circulate nutrients through the oceans (and slows Earth's rotation rate over time). These tides also provide some heat to Earth's interior—heat that helps maintain an active plate tectonic cycle. As mentioned earlier, the last step in the planet-formation process involves a larger object growing by absorbing the remaining planetesimals in its neighborhood. In Earth's case, the last major collision involved a Mars-sized object that led to the formation of the Moon.

Consider what would happen if Mars collided with Earth. What an explosion! If the collision occured under the right conditions, the iron core and heavier elements (like uranium and thorium) in Mars would incorporate into

Earth's core, and the mantle material from both bodies would mix. A significant fraction of that material would be flung into orbit around Earth and form into the Moon. Evidence from our solar system indicates that such an event actually happened. The collision obviously had a large affect on the Moon, but it also affected Earth by making it more massive (by about 10%), enriching the Earth's iron core, adding radioactive elements that heat the planet, and speeding up the rotation so that one day lasted only 5–6 hours.

Although the giant-impact scenario explains much of the data from the Earth-Moon system, scientists continue to find anomalies as they make more detailed models. For example, researchers unexpectedly found a similar composition of the Moon and Earth. The original models show that the Moon largely forms from the collider material, so it should have a different composition from Earth. However, the giant-impact model answers far more questions than its competitors.

An intriguing thought comes to mind when considering the other terrestrial planets in the solar system. Mars does have two moons, Phobos and Deimos, but they have significantly less mass and have little impact on the conditions on the red planet. Recent work indicates that the two moons likely formed from an impact that generated a third, even larger moon. However, tidal interactions with Mars over a couple million years sent the larger moon crashing back into the planet's surface, leaving only Phobos and Deimos.[5]

The collision process that produced the Moon should also occur on Venus and form debris disks there. However, Earth's sister planet has no moon. Venus does show evidence of large impacts late in its history. Venus's rotation axis is nearly sideways compared to the rest of the planets, and it rotates only once every 243 Earth days. It may be that Venus's rotation results from interactions with other planets or solar tides. Or, the last collisions may have knocked Venus's rotation axis to its weird angle and slowed its rotation rate. Yet none of these collisions produced a moon. Or maybe one collision did produce a moon, only to have a later impact cause that moon to crash back into Venus.[6]

Surveying the terrestrial planets reveals that only Earth has a large moon. Additionally, Earth's habitability may actually depend on having such a large moon!

A growing body of research indicates that events early in the solar system's history led to the formation of Earth's unusual Moon while dramatically reducing the frequency of collisions experienced by our planet. Without these two critical events, Earth's capacity to support life would have been radically diminished, maybe even to the point of being uninhabitable. Instead, Earth's history shows a remarkable string of orchestrated events leading to a place that hosts an amazing diversity and abundance of life.

Life may be diverse and abundant on Earth now, but will that continue to be the case? That question is addressed in the next chapter.

Takeaways

- Pluto's revoked planet status, although unpopular with some people, is scientifically justifiable.

- The Nice model of solar system formation has shown how the rate of asteroids and comets impacting Earth has been just-right to ensure humanity's arrival approximately 100,000 years ago.

- The giant-impact model of the Moon's formation best explains the composition of the Earth-Moon system, which dramatically affects Earth's habitability.

- Growing research shows the formation of Earth's unusual Moon and a reduction in the frequency of collisions impacting Earth, both of which have been critical to life.

Chapter 12

How Long Will Life Last?

Hollywood seems to thrive on doomsday scenarios. From an asteroid on a collision course with Earth to a genetic therapy gone awry to a catastrophic solar flare, screenwriters find numerous ways to threaten humanity's existence. Fortunately in every disaster film, something always saves humanity. In real life, the threats are much worse and offer little hope, at least for humanity on Earth. So let's survey some of the genuine and unavoidable threats to life on Earth.

The Sun Will Become One Hungry Monster

According to scientists' calculations, the observable universe contains somewhere between 10 billion trillion and 1 trillion trillion (for those who like scientific notation, that's 10^{22}–10^{24}) stars. Every one of those stars went through a phase where hydrogen fused to helium in the core of the star. For the most massive of those stars, this hydrogen-fusing phase (called the main sequence by astronomers) lasts for just a few million years, whereas the lightest stars experience life on the main sequence for more than a trillion years. For stars with a mass similar to the Sun, main-sequence life lasts about 10–11 billion years.

The Sun will continue to grow brighter for the next 5–6 billion years until it depletes the hydrogen in its core. It will then contract, causing the core to heat up dramatically. Eventually, the Sun's core temperature will rise to the point where helium can fuse into carbon. The energy released when the Sun enters this phase will cause the Sun to swell enormously. The current radius of 432,200 miles will grow to something around 90 million miles. At this radius, the Sun will engulf Mercury and Venus and likely even Earth. The exact scenario of Earth at this time is difficult to determine, but even if the Sun does not "eat" Earth, the energy increase will obliterate the atmosphere and turn the planet's surface into molten lava. Either way, life has no chance to survive.

The Sun Will Destroy Earth's Atmosphere and Oceans

Even before the Sun either eats Earth or obliterates the atmosphere, it will wreak havoc on Earth's capacity to support life. As the Sun continues to brighten over the next couple billion years, the weathering of silicate rocks will also increase. This process removes CO_2 from the atmosphere, reducing the greenhouse heating of the planet. Earth currently enjoys (and has for the last two billion years) a feedback cycle where plate tectonics, biological organisms, and weathering maintain a stable climate environment that allows life to thrive and flourish. However, plant-based life requires a minimum level of atmospheric CO_2 for photosynthesis. Within the next one billion years, diminished tectonic activity will cause the CO_2 level to drop below this minimum value and all plant-based life will perish.[1] Just for clarity, when plant-based life perishes, so too does all animal life.

Even if plant life survives dropping CO_2 levels, a global temperature increase will finish them off. Roughly 1.5 billion years from now, Earth's global temperature will rise to ~120°F (50°C). At this temperature, only the simplest life-forms—prokaryotes and protozoa—can survive. However, these higher temperatures cause water to evaporate more rapidly (it's an exponential, not a linear increase). The subsequent rise in water vapor results in a global temperature climb above the boiling point of water (212°F) over the next 200 million years. While this has catastrophic effects for most life, ultimately these temperatures mix the water higher into the atmosphere where the Sun's radiation breaks the molecules apart and the hydrogen escapes into space. The lack of water also brings plate tectonics to a grinding halt, except for volcanic activity over hot spots in the Earth's mantle. With nothing to absorb the CO_2 emitted from volcanoes, the planet will develop a thick, stifling CO_2 atmosphere. Astronomers find a similar sequence of events on Earth's sister planet, Venus.

How long will it take for all Earth's water to disappear and the planet to become completely sterilized? Less than 2.8 billion years (although the time is probably closer to 1.5 billion years).[2] No matter how we look at it, life on Earth has an expiration date. But how will Earth's life meet its demise?

Catastrophic Events That Might Wipe Out Humanity

Even under the most optimistic scenarios, the previously mentioned events will eventually kill all life on Earth. A broader range of possibilities exist that would wipe out humanity without ending all life. These events have happened in Earth's past, before humanity arrived on the scene.

Giant Asteroid Impact

Throughout the last 4.6 billion years, debris left over from the solar system's formation has collided with Earth. The most spectacular collision occurred a few hundred million years after Earth formed when a Mars-sized object slammed into the planet. This impact would have liquefied Earth's surface hundreds of miles deep and ultimately resulted in the formation of the Moon (see chapter 11). This was the largest impact, but other significant collisions have occurred. Perhaps the most well-known event took place 66 million years ago.

Right at the end of the time when dinosaurs roamed Earth, a 6-mile-wide object struck just off the Yucatán Peninsula (Mexico). As the object plowed into the peninsula, it released 420 zettajoules of energy—equivalent to 100,000 gigatons of TNT! For reference, the atomic bombs dropped during World War II had yields of 16 and 21 kilotons. The simultaneous detonation of the entire nuclear arsenal of the world would release only 10,000 megatons—10,000 times less than the event in the Yucatán Peninsula.

Aside from generating tsunamis larger than ever seen in human history, the impact made a crater (dubbed the Chicxulub crater) over 110 miles in diameter. It blew 48,000 cubic miles of sediment into the atmosphere, a significant fraction of which was ejected into space. After circulating around the globe, the ejected material heated to the point of glowing as it fell through the atmosphere and rained down on the surface of the planet. For roughly an hour, this incandescent rain heated the planet's surface to temperatures hot enough to grill steaks and ignite global wildfires.[3]

Dust and particle emissions lasted for a decade, and Earth experienced enormous increases in CO_2 as the impact vaporized carbonate rocks. Additionally, acid rain from sulfate aerosols dramatically altered the climate and decimated the food chain. It comes as no surprise that this impact coincides with the extinction of three-fourths of all plant and animal species, including the dinosaurs.[4] Scientists estimate that an impact this large happens every 50–100 million years. So, somewhere within the next 50 million years, Earth will likely experience another impact that will wipe humanity and lots of other life off the face of the planet.

Huge Volcanic Eruptions

When Mount Saint Helens erupted in 1980, it sent roughly half a cubic mile of ejecta into the atmosphere. A volcanic eruption that occurred thousands of years ago spewed 10–15 cubic miles of ash into the air. The leftover crater, Oregon's Crater Lake, contains a nearly 2,000-foot deep lake over 5 miles wide with a ring of mountains reaching over 8,000 feet above sea level. A huge magma chamber under what is now Yellowstone National Park erupted nearly 600,000 years ago, launching nearly 1,000 cubic miles of ash into the sky and leaving a caldera over 40 miles across. As powerful as these eruptions were, they pale in comparison to one that happened 250 million years ago.

In the Russian region of Siberia, a volcanic event lasting one million years deposited one million cubic miles of lava over a 2,000,000-square-mile region (about two-thirds the size of the continental United States). Given the volume of lava, it covered this region half-a-mile deep! This event also corresponds to one of the largest mass extinction events recorded in geological history. Scientists refer to the event as the "Great Dying," since over 90% of Earth's species living at the time ceased to exist. The Great Dying included the only known mass extinction of insects! The eruption likely contributed to incredible global warming such that the oceans around the equator may have reached temperatures above 100°F. For comparison, ocean temperatures at the equator typically reach only 80°F. Given the high heat capacity of water, a 20°F increase will cause lots of damage.

Large volcanic eruptions occured frequently during the last 500 million years (the time when large-bodied organisms lived on Earth). However, it's unclear when or if another catastrophically large eruption will occur. While many past volcanic events would have decimated humanity, whether such a future event will have the capacity to seriously impact human life is unknown.

Gamma-Ray Burst or Supernova Explosion
In the 1960s, the US government launched satellites capable of detecting gamma rays in order to monitor Earth's surface for nuclear tests. This period occurred in the middle of the Cold War, when the Nuclear Test-Ban Treaty with the Soviet Union had outlawed any nuclear tests—a vital component of developing new nuclear weapons. Any atmospheric or space-based tests would emit abundant gamma rays, so a system of satellites capable of measuring these gamma rays could find definitive evidence of a test. Starting in 1967, these satellites began detecting bursts of gamma rays, but the bursts looked nothing like the expected signature of nuclear tests. Over the next five years, data from additional satellites eventually constrained the source of these bursts to something outside our solar system.[5] Scientists have observed thousands of these gamma-ray bursts (GRBs) over the last few decades.

Though the true origin of GRBs remains somewhat enigmatic, scientists know a great deal about the energy released by GRBs and how a close one might impact Earth. Astronomers can detect GRBs that occurred in the distant recesses of the universe. Given the amount of radiation detected and their distance from Earth, many GRBs emit more energy in a few seconds than the Sun will emit in its 10-billion-year lifetime! Imagine what a GRB located a few light-years away would do to life on Earth.

Most of the radiation from GRBs arrives in the form of X-rays and gamma rays and lasts for a matter of seconds. With a GRB a few light-years from Earth, its highly energetic radiation will tear through Earth's atmosphere, destroying all the ozone in its path (the ozone on the other side of the planet will survive, temporarily) and breaking up the nitrogen and oxygen molecules. (For reference, nitrogen and oxygen comprise 78% and 21% of the atmosphere and consist of the diatomic molecules N_2 and O_2.) The free nitrogen and oxygen atoms will combine to make NO and NO_2. The rapid increase in these molecules will acidify the rain and also lead to more of the Sun's radiation being reflected back into space. Additionally, both NO and NO_2 catalyze the destruction of ozone. As these molecules circulate around the globe over the next few days, the remaining ozone will be severely depleted, acid rain will increase, and the globe will cool dramatically.

Once the ozone-destroying molecules are removed from the atmosphere, ozone recovery would take several years. However, ozone absorbs around 98% of the biologically damaging UV radiation emitted by the Sun before it reaches the Earth's surface. With the ozone depleted, the UV radiation will now start to destroy the biological material it impacts. Even organisms living tens of meters below the water's surface will be impacted. For example, the phytoplankton that forms the base of the marine food chain could suffer lethal doses with a 10–30% increase of UV radiation.[6]

Although studies evaluate how a GRB might affect Earth, it appears that at least one GRB actually caused some of these changes. Evidence shows that a GRB contributed significantly to the second largest extinction event in the last 500 million years. This event (second only to the Great Dying described on the previous page) occurred during the end of the Ordovician Period 440 million years ago. More than half the marine genera and 80% of the marine species went extinct, accompanied by massive glaciations and rapidly falling sea levels. The pattern of extinction provides good evidence that a GRB contributed significantly to, if not caused, the event.[7]

Estimates of GRB rates indicate that between one and a few of these bursts should happen close to the Earth every billion years. During the Ordovician extinction, no large, land-dwelling creatures lived. Given the damage a GRB event caused even to life partially shielded by the oceans, if one occurred now it would exterminate humanity, as well as lots of other life.

It's the End of the Universe as We Know It

Scientists have long contemplated the universe's ultimate fate: heat death. But what exactly is "heat death"? Life requires the universe to contain regions that are hotter than others because life extracts energy as the heat moves from hot to cold regions. Eventually all of the energy will be extracted and the universe will reach thermal equilibrium. When that day finally comes, every part of the universe will have the same temperature and will therefore be unable to support life. However, this won't happen for hundreds of billions or trillions of years.[8]

A more immediate concern relates to the stability of the space-time fabric itself. In 2012, scientists announced the discovery of the long-sought-after Higgs boson (subatomic particle) and found it had a mass roughly 126 times the mass of a proton. This measurement brought a bit of unexpected news. Using the Higgs mass and the mass of the top quark (another subatomic particle postulated in 1973 and discovered in 1995), scientists determined that the fundamental fabric of our universe may reside in an unstable state.[9] Given enough time, the fabric could decay to a more stable state. Normally "stable" is a good thing, but the transition from the current state to the more stable state will literally destroy the universe as we know it. Planets, stars, and galaxies will disappear, atoms will disintegrate, and all the structure in the universe will turn into pure energy. Once some region begins to decay to a lower-energy state, the obliteration of our universe will spread from that place traveling at the speed of light.[10] The best calculations indicate this won't happen for *at least* a few billion years, but it could have already started. Once it starts, nothing will stop it and we would have no warning when it hits.

The Bottom Line

Life has flourished on Earth for billions of years and the conditions on the planet today easily support advanced life like humans. Catastrophic events have dramatically reshaped the planet over this time, but life still thrived. In fact, an impressively diverse array of life fills the planet. Yet, inevitable events in the future will bring life to an end. The only way to avoid this conclusion, at least temporarily, would be to export life to some other planet. Such an endeavor likely will remain beyond humanity's reach. However, the fact that life has an "expiration date" finds a comfortable overlap with the biblical idea of an end time.

We will discuss more theistic implications in coming chapters. For now, we need to assess where we are in our appreciation or lack thereof for Earth as a rare place for life. What has the evidence shown so far? Next, we will continue our exoplanet exploration by taking a look at systems with more than one star.

 Takeaways

- Life on Earth has an expiration date; the Sun will eventually destroy Earth's atmosphere and oceans and kill all life in about 2.8 billion years.

- A giant asteroid struck Earth 66 million years ago and led to the extinction of three-fourths of all plant and animal species; this kind of event happens every 50–100 million years.

- A large volcanic eruption caused the "Great Dying," which brought 90% of Earth's species to extinction, including insects.

- Gamma ray bursts or supernova explosions also pose a threat to human civilization, and they have both occurred in the past.

- The stability of the space-time fabric of the universe itself may decay— destroying the universe and all life.

- An end to the universe is consistent with the biblical idea of an end time.

Chapter 13

Is *Star Wars* Realistic?

A young Luke Skywalker longs to leave his home planet and join his friends at the academy, but he has just learned that he must remain stuck on Tatooine with his aunt and uncle for yet another farming season. Dejected and feeling like he's going nowhere, Luke emerges from his house and stares wistfully at the magnificent binary sunset sinking into the Tatooine desert. Just as Luke comes to the crushing realization that his dreams are slowly slipping away, John Williams's stirring score reaches a crescendo.

The "binary sunset" scene is arguably one of the most iconic moments from *Star Wars*. One of the many reasons for this scene's appeal is its relatability. (I can certainly relate to having outside influences squash my dreams or impede my progress.) Another reason for the scene's appeal is its realistic visual effect of twin suns. But how realistic is a double star sunset like the one Luke sees? Fortunately, exoplanet discoveries in the past decade help illuminate the answer and provide insight into our ongoing habitability search.

Is Luke's Sunset Realistic?
During one of the sessions at the June 2016 American Astronomical Society meeting a presenter announced the discovery of a planet orbiting two stars. Dubbed Kepler-1647b, the planet set many records. Coming in with a radius 6% larger than Jupiter (and a mass 50% larger), Kepler-1647b was the largest transiting planet discovered orbiting binary stars. The planet takes 1,107 days to complete an orbit, giving it the longest period of any transiting exoplanet![1] The binary system that the planet orbits formed 4.4 billion years ago, demonstrating the long-term stability of the system. Additionally, Kepler-1647b orbits in the habitable zone of its binary host stars. However, because its mass and radius are similar to Jupiter, Kepler-1647b offers no hope of harboring life.

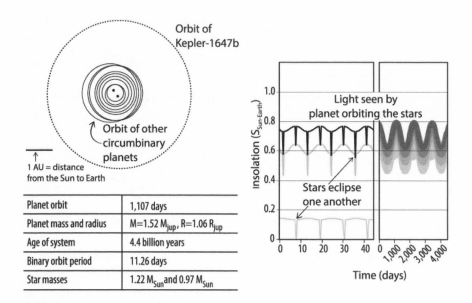

Figure 13.1: Orbit of Kepler-1647b

Although Kepler-1647b's existence shows some plausibility of Luke's binary sunset, many other factors dramatically affect the possibility. In order to make some estimate of its likelihood, astronomers need to know (1) how often binary stars occur (and the general dynamics of binary systems), (2) how the binary system affects the stability of any planets that might form, and (3) what kinds of planets might form around binary stars. Let's look at each factor.

How Many Stars Are Binaries?

Our galaxy contains somewhere between 200 and 400 billion stars (that's about 50 stars for every person living on Earth!). The smallest stars would fit within a moderate-sized city, about 10–15 miles across. The largest stars, if placed at the center of the solar system, would engulf Mercury, Venus, Earth, Mars, and even the asteroid belt. These examples showcase the extreme ways that stars die after they exhaust their hydrogen fuel but they represent only a few percent of the stars in the Milky Way Galaxy (MWG).

Considering stars like the Sun that fuse hydrogen as the main fuel source (what astronomers refer to as "main sequence" stars) still gives quite a range of stellar properties. The most massive main sequence stars (those with masses

Mass (solar units)	Luminosity (solar units)	Lifetime	Fraction (%)
0.08–0.45	<0.08	5,500–70 Gyr	76.45
0.45–0.8	0.08–0.6	70–17 Gyr	12.1
0.8–1.04	0.6–1.5	17–9 Gyr	7.6
1.04–1.4	1.5–5	9–4 Gyr	3
1.4–2.1	2–25	4–1.5 Gyr	0.6
2.1–16	25–30,000	1,500–10 Myr	0.13
>16	>30,000	<10 Myr	0.00003

Table 13.1: Star Parameters by Category

hundreds of times that of the Sun) will exhaust their hydrogen fuel in a few million years before becoming black holes or neutron stars. The least massive (those with a tenth the mass of the Sun) will fuse hydrogen for more than a trillion years.

Astronomers worked diligently over the past two centuries to provide an accurate survey of the types of stars in the MWG, as well as how many of those stars reside in binary systems. As expected, the most massive stars are easiest to find and characterize. The first systematic attempts to study the frequency of binaries in stars with masses similar to the Sun found that 65–80% of these stars have partners. Continuing research showed that the fraction of binaries increases with the mass of the star. However, the distribution of stars acts like tornadoes, earthquakes, and floods. The largest ones are the easiest to see, but the rate increases exponentially as the size decreases. For example, star masses range from one-tenth to 100 times the mass of the Sun. Thinking linearly, one would conclude that the Sun is a runt, with many stars having larger masses. As it turns out, more than 90% of stars have masses smaller than the Sun and stars with less mass may come in pairs only one third of the time.[2]

Putting all this information together gives a picture where the most common type of star has a mass noticeably less than the Sun and likely exists as a lone star. As the stellar mass increases, becoming more Sun-like, the number of stars decreases and each likely has a companion.

Binaries Affect Planetary Orbits

Binary systems increase the types of possible orbits. So, before addressing the frequency of planets orbiting binary systems, we first need to examine how the dynamics of those systems affect the possible planetary orbits.

Binary stars, even without considering planets, exist in a range of orbits as shown in figure 13.2. For a potentially habitable planet to survive on a stable orbit, the gravitational influences from the two stars must be consistent. This requires nearly circular star orbits (around the center of mass) that never approach the liquid water habitable zone. Two options remain: the stars must orbit with either very small or very large separations. For very small separations, the potentially habitable planet would orbit both stars (and give a view similar to Luke's epic sunset). For large separations, the planet would orbit one or the other as shown in figure 13.2.

Some studies show that as many as 50–60% of binary systems fall into one of these two configurations in such a way that a planet could orbit in the liquid water habitable zone (see chapter 7).[3] However, other studies indicate that most planetary systems orbiting one star of a widely separated binary experience gravitational disruptions over a few billion years.[4] In fact, disruptions that break-up the binary system may explain the perplexing observation of planets that orbit their host stars with misaligned orbits.[5] The dynamics of star and planet formation (see chapter 11) mean that a planet should orbit around the same axis about which the star spins. For a growing number of exoplanets, these two axes are badly misaligned. In some cases, Jupiter-sized exoplanets even orbit in the wrong direction ("retrograde" in astronomy-speak)!

Fraction of Binaries and Exoplanets

At this step in the search for exoplanets around binary stars, the situation gets more complicated for many reasons. Finding planets around close binary stars (where the exoplanet orbits both stars in the binary system) poses problems not seen for single stars. For the transit method, the dynamics of gravitationally interacting bodies (the binary stars and the orbiting exoplanet) causes variations in the timing of the transits. When the exoplanet orbits very close to the stars, the transits occur more often. Hence, astronomers get the necessary data to sort out the variations and confirm the existence of an exoplanet. However, for orbits like Kepler-1647b that take hundreds and thousands of days, it takes far longer to get adequate data. Similar difficulties affect the radial velocity technique.

Assessing the fraction of exoplanets that orbit only one star of the binary

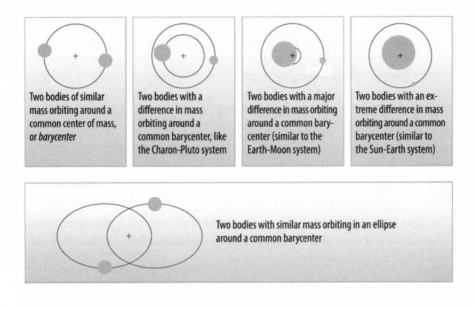

Figure 13.2: Possible Binary Orbits

system seems easier. Surveys of the stars known to host exoplanets show that roughly half of all known exoplanets (at least those detected by the transit method using the *Kepler*) exist in wide binary star systems.[6] Although compelling from an astronomy perspective, this fact does not address Luke's chance of gazing wistfully into the twin suns of Tatooine.

The Bottom Line

Clearly binary star systems host exoplanets! Most research to date focuses on Jupiter-sized exoplanets because they are the easiest to detect, but it seems reasonable to conclude that Earth-sized planets will also exist in binary star systems. At this time, it even appears that binary stars host planets as frequently as single stars, although this may change as astronomers accumulate more data and make more precise measurements.

The existence of Earth-sized planets orbiting around binary stars is only one factor in the equation though. *The big question remains whether a truly habitable planet can develop in such a scenario.* One huge factor in Earth's ongoing habitability is the incredible coordination between the increasing output from the Sun and the changes in Earth's atmosphere and surface. Two stars with changing luminosity will require even more fine-tuning to the exoplanet's atmosphere, and chapter 14 explores that demand in more detail.

In the next chapter, we will touch briefly on a question that inevitably arises when people consider life, alien life, and exoplanets. Some people say we have not been good caretakers of this planet and that Earth is warming at an alarming rate. We'll address these concerns in a manner consistent with our planetary studies.

 Takeaways ─────────────────────────────

- In 2016 astronomers announced the discovery of a planet orbiting a binary system that was stable and in the habitable zone; nevertheless, it offered no hope of harboring life.

- Systematic attempts to study the frequency of binaries in stars with masses similar to the Sun found a rate of about 65–80%.

- Finding planets around binaries is not as straightforward as detecting them orbiting a single star.

- It seems reasonable to conclude that Earth-sized planets exist in binary systems, but that does not mean a truly habitable planet can develop in such systems.

Chapter 14

Is Global Warming Bad?

Want to stir up controversy? Just make a definitive statement about global warming, either good or bad. Chances are high that someone will strongly disagree. The scientific data demonstrates pretty conclusively that Earth's surface temperature has risen by 1°F over the last 40 years. Though widespread consensus exists regarding the temperature rise, major disagreements occur when discussing the *cause* of this warming. Is it a result of changing astronomical conditions like fluctuating galactic cosmic rays or variability in the distance from the Sun? What effect does variability in atmospheric processes and ocean circulation play? What about aerosols and particulates in the atmosphere? Are greenhouse gases, particularly those generated by humanity (like carbon dioxide and methane), the cause of the temperature rise? Have humans made any contribution to the warming? The short answer is "Yes!" All of these factors affect the global temperature.

Political positions seem to play an inordinate role in the public discussion of global warming. Still, a short chapter in a book focused on a different topic is not the ideal place to delve into the complex scientific findings. Rather than enter that minefield, I want to address the importance of global warming in an entirely different context—how Earth's atmosphere plays a critical and fundamental role in the planet's capacity to host a teeming and diverse array of life.

Putting Things in Perspective
The worst-case scenarios typically have temperature increases around 10°F over the next few centuries. Clearly such an increase would have a major impact on the planet, but consider this number from a different perspective. What would Earth's average global temperature be without any greenhouse gas-induced warming? A bone-chilling 0°F! That's an arctic winter kind of cold and well below the actual value of 60°F. What makes the difference? An abundance

of greenhouse gases in Earth's atmosphere.

Basic Principles of Greenhouse Heating

Earth's surface receives a known quantity of energy from the Sun: 240 W/m². (This chapter needs some equations to establish the important points about Earth's atmosphere. When you encounter an equation in a paragraph, feel free to skip to the last sentence or two; that's where the key principle involved will be delineated.) Because Earth's surface is in equilibrium, it also radiates this much energy back into space. Using the Stefan-Boltzmann law, we can calculate the temperature that corresponds to this amount of energy radiation. For those who like equations, $S = \sigma T^4$, where S is power per unit area, σ is the Stefan-Boltzmann constant, and T is the absolute temperature. Plugging in S = 240 W/m², $\sigma = 5.67 \times 10^{-8}$ W/m²/T⁴ and solving gives T = 255°K. Converting to more familiar units yields the temperature of 0°F mentioned on page 121. However, adding an atmosphere changes the picture.

Most of the radiation Earth receives from the Sun arrives in the form of visible light. The gases in Earth's largely transparent atmosphere allow the Sun's light to penetrate to Earth's surface where it is absorbed and heats up the surface. The surface then radiates its energy back toward space as heat. However, this heat radiation may or may not pass through the atmosphere, depending on the gases present. The two gases that dominate Earth's atmosphere—nitrogen (78%) and oxygen (21%)—allow the heat radiation to pass unaffected. Other natural gases (water vapor, carbon dioxide, methane, nitrous oxide, and ozone) and man-made gases (chlorofluorocarbons and hydrofluorocarbons) have molecular structures that will absorb the heat radiation coming from Earth's surface and heat up the atmosphere. Just like the surface, the atmosphere will reradiate this energy eventually. Unlike the surface, some will radiate to space, and some will radiate toward the surface, resulting in an increased surface temperature. Getting all the details exactly right requires fairly complicated calculations, but the net result is a life-friendly surface temperature of 60°F.

The higher the concentration of greenhouse gases in the atmosphere, the more warming happens at the planet's surface. For the last 500 million years, when large-bodied animals roamed the Earth, oxygen and nitrogen dominated the gas budget of the atmosphere. Conspicuously, the greenhouse gases that make Earth so habitable comprise just a tiny part of the atmosphere, less than a fraction of a percent. This fact stands out when compared to the composition of the atmospheres of Mars and Venus. With miniscule amounts of oxygen, nitrogen adds about 3% for each planet. Carbon dioxide dominates both atmospheres with over 95%! Additionally, the atmosphere on Venus is 90 times more dense than Earth's. Consequently, Earth's sister planet has a surface temperature around 864°F—so hot that paper would spontaneously combust, if Venus's atmosphere had any oxygen. The global surface temperature of -67°F on Mars results from an atmospheric density less than 1% of Earth's and its larger distance from the Sun.

Water vapor, by far the largest contributor to Earth's temperate climate, receives very little press in the current discussions about global warming. In fairness though, humans have little control over the amount of water vapor and a much larger influence over carbon dioxide, methane, and the particulate matter in the atmosphere.

What about Earth's Atmosphere in the Past?

Humanity's relatively small contributions to the global climate and possible consequences point to a rather astonishing fact about Earth's climate. For the vast majority of the last four billion years, Earth's global temperature remained conducive to liquid water on the planet's surface. Although that may seem a mundane fact, Earth has undergone major changes that could have (and maybe should have) either frozen all the water or boiled the oceans away!

Major Changes in the Sun . . .

Currently, Earth's surface receives an average of 240 W/m² of energy from the Sun. However, the energy emitted by the Sun and received by Earth varies over time. In order to understand how important these changes are, let's use the amount of radiation received at Earth's surface to calculate the amount of radiation emitted by the Sun. We will use Earth's average distance from the Sun, since this corresponds to astronomers' calculations of whether an exoplanet resides in the "habitable zone." First, the atmosphere and surface reflect an average of 103 W/m². Adding that to the amount received from the Sun (240 W/m²) results in 343 W/m². However, that is the average value over Earth's surface, so we must multiply by a factor of Earth's surface area divided by the area covered by Earth, or $(4\pi R_E^2)/(\pi R_E^2)$ where R_E = Earth's radius. After all these conversions, the amount of energy received by Earth at one astronomical unit (the average distance from the Sun to Earth) is 1,361 W/m². Satellite measurements show this value varies by 0.1% over the solar magnetic cycle (think sunspots) and by no more than 0.2% over the last 400 years. This means that the Sun's output is stable to a fraction of a percent over the last few centuries.

Over the past million years, the amount of solar radiation received at the top of the atmosphere has varied around its current value by about 10%. Note that the Sun's output was largely constant (although it grew slightly, about 0.01%), but the amount of radiation hitting the planet changed because of variations in the Earth-Sun distance and the orientation of Earth's spin axis. During this period the global temperature cycled between its current value and 20°F lower, with a periodicity of 100,000 years. The times of lower temperatures brought glacial advances covering North America, Europe, and Asia. The dramatic changes in Earth's climate arose not because of changes in the Sun, but simply due to variations in Earth's orbit. Even during these glaciations, abundant oceans covered the surface.

As far back as 3.8 billion years ago, geological evidence shows that oceans covered the surface of the planet. Hints of liquid water exist from more than 4 billion years ago, but none of the pristine crustal material from that time still exists—tectonic activity has recycled it. Water's presence in the form of oceans means that Earth's global temperature remained within about 20°F (either higher or lower) of its current value. But 4 billion years ago, the Sun emitted 30% less radiation than it does today! If a periodic change of 10% in the amount of solar radiation Earth receives causes large glacial cycles, imagine how a Sun with two-thirds the output would affect Earth's climate. The fact that oceans covered the planet over the last 4 billion years means something compensated for the dimmer Sun.

. . . Require Major Changes in the Earth's Atmosphere . . .
Not only has the Sun's output changed dramatically over the last 4 billion years, but so has Earth's atmosphere. Though all the details are hard to pin down, one major difference between today's atmosphere and the one 4 billion years ago relates to the amount of oxygen present. Numerous geological features demonstrate that no free oxygen existed until about 2.5 billion years ago. While oxygen plays no role in greenhouse heating, it does affect at least one significant greenhouse gas—methane.

For the last 3.5 billion years ancient microbes that emit methane lived on Earth. Because methanogens thrive in hydrothermal vent environments, some scientists think they may have been the first life-forms on Earth.[1] Whether the first life or later arrivals, these organisms began pumping this potent greenhouse gas into the atmosphere. Scientists do not have good tools to determine the ancient concentration of atmospheric methane, but even fractions of a percent would warm the surface of early Earth. A significant greenhouse effect from methane probably resulted in the reduced emission from a dimmer Sun being more effective at heating early Earth to support liquid oceans.

Roughly 2.5 billion years ago, microbial life produced enough oxygen to start filling the atmosphere. Free oxygen is highly reactive, so it quickly combined with the methane to make carbon dioxide (CO_2) and water. Since the greenhouse effect of methane greatly exceeds that of the CO_2 and water vapor, the planet cooled dramatically. The cooling brought more snowfall and, since snow reflects more sunlight than land or ocean, the planet's decreased absorption of solar energy caused even more cooling. That brought even more snowfall, causing glaciers to advance almost to the equator! This massive glaciation event, called the Huronian glaciation, lasted for 200 million years!

After this time, oxygen comprised at least a few percent of the atmosphere. Around one billion years ago, the oxygen content started increasing to levels more similar to current values. Once again, this increase in oxygen was accompanied by another snowball event where glaciers advanced to nearly cover the Earth. For both snowball events, the breakup of a supercontinent that existed at the time and the action of a robust carbonate-silicate cycle (see chapter 5) dumped a lot of greenhouse gases (mostly carbon dioxide) into the atmosphere. The additional greenhouse heating from these gases brought Earth out of these massive glaciations. One indisputable fact about these atmospheric changes is this: without the increase of oxygen, no life beyond single-celled organisms would live on Earth.

. . . And Major Changes in the Earth's Oceans

When we think of oceans, the image that typically comes to mind is one of cobalt blue waters covering the earth. The lack of oxygen on early Earth led to a much different picture. The abundance of dissolved iron in the oceans would have given them a light green color rather than the usual blue waters,. As oxygen-producing bacteria increased in the oceans, the iron would have precipitated out and developed banded-iron formations that contain most of the commercial iron ore available on Earth.

Perhaps the largest change to occur in the oceans was the development of continents. Oceans almost completely covered early Earth's surface. (Volcanic activity likely pushed a few islands above the surface.) In contrast, continents make up a large fraction of Earth's surface today—roughly 30%. Chapter 5 describes the critical role of plate tectonics for a habitable planet, but one aspect is relevant here.

The movement of plates around Earth's surface has generated an enduring set of continents where most of life lives and thrives. Continental crust material is less dense than oceanic crust, so the continents float on the oceanic crust. The movement of the plates recycles the oceanic crust relatively quickly (geologically speaking) but continental crust sticks around much longer. The oldest oceanic crust material dates to 250 million years ago, but continental rocks date to 4 billion years ago. Zircons in the continental crust date even farther back—4.4 billion years ago.[2] Dating of material around the globe shows that the continental crust tends to cluster around dates of 1.2, 1.9, 2.7, and 3.3 billion years ago. This clustering indicates that the continents grew in bursts during the middle portion of Earth's history (although it may result from preferential preservation of crust that grew uniformly).[3]

Continents affect the planet's temperature in at least three important ways. First, the amount of continental crust, as well as its location and orientation, plays an important role in how the oceans circulate and move heat around the planet. Second, continents expose rocks to the atmosphere. The atmosphere reacts with the continents through various means in ways that change the composition of the atmosphere, specifically the amount of greenhouse gases. Third, and perhaps most importantly, the continents provide the habitat for more than two-thirds of the life on Earth and that life dramatically affects the atmosphere. Some of those life-forms produce oxygen and consume carbon dioxide while other organisms reverse the process. Undoubtedly, the dramatic change of the types of life on Earth also affects the global temperature of the planet.

The Bottom Line
Earth has sustained huge changes over the last 4.5 billion years. A much dimmer Sun has grown steadily brighter. The surface changed from being covered in oceans to having a large fraction of continents (and the oceans changed too). The atmosphere went from having no free oxygen to containing an abundance of oxygen that advanced life requires. Life went from relatively simple, single-celled creatures to an incredibly diverse array of life. Every one of these changes had the potential to alter the planet's temperature to an uninhabitable wasteland. Instead, each step of the process maintained the temperate environment required for life and built Earth's capacity to support life. In other words, global warming got us to where we are today.

If climate change considerations are not enough to raise eyebrows, then suggesting that life can *only* be found on Earth is the mark of hubris. Skeptics sometimes charge Bible-believing Christians with haughtiness for saying God created life solely on this planet. Is the criticism deserved? We'll address this hotly debated question in the next chapter.

Takeaways _____

- Without any greenhouse gas-induced warming, Earth's average global temperature would be near 0°F.

- The largest contributor to Earth's temperate climate is water vapor, over which humans have little control.

- A study of Earth's history reveals that changes in the Sun, the oceans, and the atmosphere both caused and brought Earth out of massive glaciations while increasing the oxygen level such that life beyond single-celled organisms became possible.

- Continents (and the continental shelves) affect the temperature of the planet in at least three ways, including providing a habitat for more than two-thirds of species on Earth.

- Each step of the physical process over billions of years could have led to an uninhabitable wasteland for Earth, but instead it maintained a temperate climate suitable for advanced life.

Chapter 15

Isn't It Arrogant to Think
We Are the Only Life?

About 15 minutes into a talk given to the Richard Dawkins Foundation, physicist Lawrence Krauss made this provocative statement:

> The amazing thing is that every atom in your body came from a star that exploded. And, the atoms in your left hand probably came from a different star than your right hand. It really is the most poetic thing I know about physics: You are all stardust. You couldn't be here if stars hadn't exploded, because the elements—the carbon, nitrogen, oxygen, iron, all the things that matter for evolution—weren't created at the beginning of time. They were created in the nuclear furnaces of stars, and the only way they could get into your body is if those stars were kind enough to explode. So, forget Jesus. The stars died so that you could be here today.[1]

Krauss's opening line likely doesn't apply to the abundant hydrogen atoms in your body, but that minor quibble in no way negates the two main points that Krauss makes. First, the elements life depend on—carbon, oxygen, nitrogen, and others—all formed in the blazing furnaces at the center of every star. Second, those elements would have remained in the stars without some mechanism to eject the elements back into space where other stars would form. Putting aside the snarky, irreverent comment regarding Jesus, Krauss articulates one of the reasons many scientists believe we are not alone in the universe.

Are We Special?
According to the popular narrative, any idea that humanity is special goes against the progress of scientific discovery. For centuries, people thought Earth resided at the center of the solar system—and consequently the universe. Then,

in the middle 1500s, Nicolaus Copernicus dethroned Earth from its special, central location to one shared by a host of planets that revolve around the Sun. An abundance of evidence since Copernicus's discovery demonstrates that Earth indisputably orbits around the Sun, but the idea that this placement represents a demotion seems like a twentieth century reinterpretation of history.[2]

Better scientific understanding has now demonstrated that the Sun is one of hundreds of billions of stars in the Milky Way Galaxy. Our galaxy is just one of hundreds of billions of galaxies in the observable universe and may reside in one of an uncountable number of universes that forever lay beyond our detection. Clearly, Earth occupies no special location in the universe—at least not in terms of physical space. In the 1900s, scientists formalized this idea and termed it the Copernican principle (or principle of mediocrity). This principle plays an important role in helping us understand the development of the universe.

To many scientists, it seems logical to extend the Copernican principle and draw the conclusion that nothing about humanity is special. This extension, if correct, means that the universe should be teeming with inhabited planets much like Earth. Although scientists see no evidence of life beyond Earth yet, perhaps they will find that the universe teems with life. But Christianity has never based humanity's value on our location. Instead, our value comes from the fact that we are made in God's image, and that will not change if God created life somewhere else in the universe.

Before proceeding, one comment is in order. From a Christian perspective, arguing that life is unique to Earth does not arise from arrogance. Christianity does not say, "Humans are so important, therefore, there is no other life in the universe." According to the Bible, the only reason humanity has any significance is because God made us in his image and endows us with value. In fact, the central message of Christianity is that apart from God, humanity has no reason for boasting (for example, see Ephesians 2:8–9).

So let's clarify the question. Most people want to know: Given the presence of life here on Earth, does it make more sense to conclude that God brought it about or that it arose in the absence of God? Many think that finding life throughout the universe would indicate that God is not necessary to explain the presence of life here on Earth. So what reasons do naturalists give for thinking life permeates the universe?

The Most Abundant Materials

Scientists have developed a set of tools to understand how the universe changed from its earliest moments to the spectacular wonder we see today. Using those tools reveals that the most abundant elements in the universe find a close parallel to the most abundant elements used by life. For example, the most abundant chemically active elements in the universe (by mass-fraction) are hydrogen, oxygen, carbon, iron, and nitrogen.[3] The same list for living organisms includes oxygen, carbon, hydrogen, and nitrogen. In other words, the most essential elements of life are the most common elements in the universe.

Virtually every scientist recognizes the importance of water for life (see chapter 4). Perhaps it may come as a surprise to know that water is the third most abundantly produced molecule in the universe. First is hydrogen (which dominantly exists as a diatomic molecule, H_2) followed by its protonated form, H_3^+. Since hydrogen and oxygen are among the most abundant elements, the universe readily produces water, arguably the most important molecule required for life.

Prior to 1992, scientists knew of only eight planets (although they mistakenly included Pluto as a ninth, see chapter 11), and all those orbited the Sun. Since that time they have discovered thousands of planets beyond the solar system. Though the ability to detect Earth-like planets around Sun-like stars sits right at the edge of our technical capabilities, strong evidence exists that Earth-sized planets abound in the universe. On average, each star in the sky contains at least one Earth-sized planet.

Since the universe readily produces the building blocks of life (rocky planets, water, and the necessary elements), many people ask why we think that life exists only here on Earth? In response, many Christians argue that the bulk of the scientific evidence points to a universe and Earth that look designed to support life (and that life itself looks designed). Specifically, as scientists understand more about how the universe began and developed, they find a wealth of evidence that the universe looks designed to produce the building blocks of life. Here are a few examples.

The String of Unexpected Discoveries
Although the main elements of life match the most abundant elements of the universe, the processes that formed those elements are rather unexpected. One might even say they looked designed.

In the Beginning . . .
Nearly 14 billion years ago, the known universe came into existence via the "big bang." The unbelievably hot temperatures and densities made the early

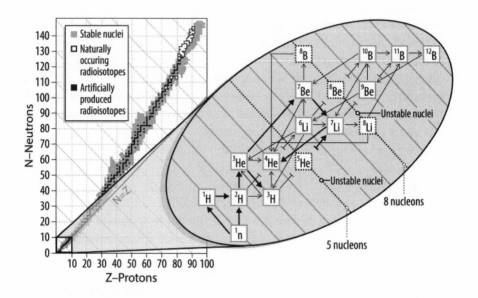

Figure 15.1: Plot of Stable Nuclei, Especially for Small Numbers of Nucleons
Note that no stable nuclei exist that have 5 or eight nucleons (protons plus neutrons).

universe unrecognizable compared to today, but things began to quickly take shape. Roughly 10 seconds after the big bang, the universe consisted of protons, neutrons, and electrons—at least concerning the ordinary matter of our familiar world. Over the next few minutes, as the temperature continued to cool, the protons and neutrons assembled into some heavier nuclei, mainly helium. At this point, the composition of the universe was 75% hydrogen, 25% helium-4, 0.01% deuterium and helium-3, and trace amounts (10^{-8}%) of heavier elements like lithium-7. However, slight changes in the strengths of the electromagnetic and nuclear interactions would have led to a much different reality.

As protons and neutrons collided, they fused together to make heavier elements. The slowest step in this process was the formation of a deuteron (one proton and one neutron). Once sufficient quantities of deuterons existed, they quickly added more neutrons and protons until something else stopped the sequence. As figure 15.1 shows, elements with lots of protons and neutrons exist. While the process would naturally stop at the formation of iron (since adding more protons or neutrons beyond this element consumes energy instead of producing energy), ending the chain at iron would likely leave no hydrogen left over. Fortunately, the laws of physics "conspired" to ensure the universe would contain plenty of hydrogen.

Producing an Abundance of Hydrogen

The diagonal lines in figure 15.1 represent nuclei with the same number of nucleons (nucleons = protons + neutrons). Figure 15.1 inset zooms in on the region with small amounts of protons and neutrons. The solid boxes are stable nuclei where the dashed boxes are nuclei with short half-lives (less than one second). Notice that no stable nuclei exist for nucleon numbers 5 or 8. These two gaps stopped the fusion chain during the first few minutes after the big bang and resulted in a universe with lots of helium and an abundance of hydrogen.

Not only do the laws of physics governing the stability of nuclei cause the 5- and 8-nucleon gaps, but also they prevent other catastrophes that would remove all hydrogen. Because the neutron is heavier than a proton, fewer neutrons formed in comparison to protons as the universe cooled. Free neutrons also decay with a half-life of 10 minutes, further reducing the neutron-to-proton ratio. If protons existed in the same ratio during this period of fusion, all the protons would fuse to deuterium, leaving none of the single-proton forms of hydrogen. More importantly, if a nucleus with just two protons were stable, all the protons necessary for hydrogen atoms would fuse into this diproton state. Yet, the laws of physics produced a sufficiently small neutron-to-proton ratio and an unstable diproton nucleus.

What are the two most-known chemical compounds? Clearly, water (H_2O) takes first place, but with all the discussion of global warming, carbon dioxide (CO_2) probably comes in a close second. Curiously, the existence of carbon dioxide also depends on a careful balance of the laws of physics.

Producing an Abundance of Carbon

Remember, the only elements in the universe a few minutes after the big bang were hydrogen and helium (and miniscule amounts of lithium and beryllium). Not until a few hundred million years later did stars that could make heavier elements form. Most stars fuse hydrogen into helium, but some are large enough to fuse helium into carbon. Fusion requires two nuclei (each with a positive charge) to join together. Consequently, the strength of the strong nuclear and electromagnetic forces affects how the process works and what configurations of protons and neutrons are stable. Carbon production requires three helium nuclei to come together at the same time—an extremely unlikely event, but three "coincidences" ensure adequate carbon in the universe. (Keep in mind that we are covering necessary scientific ground with the initial question about arrogance in view.)

Coincidence #1: Beryllium-8

As it turns out, two helium nuclei will stick together for a little while (making a semi-stable beryllium-8 nucleus). If beryllium-8 (Be^8) were truly stable, virtually all the helium would form beryllium-8, leaving none available to make carbon. As Fred Hoyle noted:

> Had Be^8 been stable, the helium-burning reaction would have been so violent that stellar evolution—with its consequent nucleosynthesis—would have been very limited in scope, less *interesting* in its effect.... if there was little carbon in the world compared to oxygen, it is likely that living creatures could never have developed.[4]

However, if beryllium-8 were not semi-stable, stars would produce an insignificant amount of carbon. The strong nuclear and electromagnetic forces combine to give beryllium-8 the stability necessary for stars to form significant amounts of carbon, but not quite enough for life.

Coincidence #2: Carbon Energy Level Resonance

The carbon nucleus has an energy level that sits just above the combined energy of a beryllium-8 and helium nucleus. This causes a resonance that dramatically increases the rate of carbon production. For an analogy, consider pushing someone on a swing. If you give small pushes at random times, the swing remains almost at a standstill, but if you push at the just-right period; that is, at the resonant frequency, the swing will go higher and higher. Consequently, the rate of carbon formation occurs more rapidly because of this resonance than if the energy level were either far from or below the combined energy of the beryllium-8 and helium nucleus.

Coincidence #3: No Oxygen Resonance

Clearly life requires carbon, but it also needs oxygen. The energy levels in oxygen provide the third "coincidence" necessary for the universe to contain sufficient carbon for life. The interiors of stars (where this fusion occurs) reach temperatures difficult to imagine: over 100,000,000°C! The temperature required for carbon production matches that for carbon to join with helium to make oxygen. The reaction that fuses carbon and helium happens at a sufficient rate to produce the oxygen required by life. If oxygen had a resonant energy level similar to carbon, all the carbon produced in stars would immediately fuse into oxygen. However, the relevant energy level in oxygen is just below the combined energy of a carbon and helium nucleus. Thus, large stars produce sufficient quantities of oxygen *and* carbon.

Scientists have understood the basic theoretical framework to explain the production of carbon and oxygen for decades, and recent efforts calculate key elements of this framework from the fundamental elements of the universe.[5] Given this knowledge, scientists can analyze how the universe would differ as the strength of the strong nuclear and electromagnetic forces change.

A paper published by physicist Max Tegmark graphs such an analysis showing that small changes in the strengths of these forces result in a universe incapable of hosting life (see figure 15.2[6]). More importantly, the configuration of the forces that permit features essential to life (stable carbon, stars, hydrogen) matches the requirements for the triple coincidence necessary for producing carbon and oxygen in stars.

Reflecting on these coincidences, Fred Hoyle commented, "a common sense interpretation of the facts suggests that a superintellect has monkeyed with physics, as well as with chemistry and biology." I would agree. These discoveries demonstrate scientists' ability to explain how the universe produced the carbon and oxygen necessary for life. The remarkable aspect of this knowledge relates to the fact that the laws of physics match the only configuration of those laws that permit life.

Some might respond that this fine-tuning is just a selection effect; the laws of physics *had* to take some form and then life developed based on the result. However, the fine-tuning shows more sophistication. It's not that any set of elements would do. Rather, water and carbon both exhibit an extraordinary set of characteristics that life requires to flourish. That the laws of physics takes a form that not only permits the existence of hydrogen, carbon, and oxygen, but also facilitates and even drives their production indicates that the universe is designed with a purpose.

Beyond the fine-tuning seen in the laws of physics, one can argue that the constraints imposed by life provide evidence that Earth was designed to support life. Chapters 5, 7, 11, 12, 13, and 14 describe some of the constraints on a life-supporting planet.

Going back to the question at hand, is it arrogant to think that we are

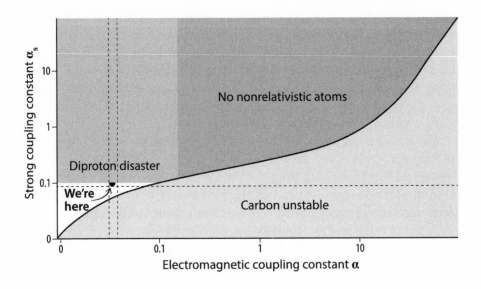

Figure 15.2: Strong Nuclear and Electromagnetic Force-Comparison of Effect on Life
Only the region labeled "We're Here" allows the formation of all the elements essential to life. Note the logarithmic scales on both axes.

alone? Good reasons exist to think that life might permeate the universe. On the other hand, evidence points to a universe and Earth designed for life. Are these two notions at odds with each other? I don't think so, but it really doesn't matter what I think. Rather than deciding the question based on motives (in this case, arrogance), science provides a set of tools to acquire the data to answer the question.

Science can weigh in, but so can theology. Specifically, people want to know if the Bible claims that there is no other life out there. We take a look at that question in the next chapter.

 Takeaways _____

- Many modern scientists operate with an assumed Copernican principle, meaning that humans are not special. In line with this principle, the universe readily produces life's essential needs—rocky planets, water, and the necessary elements.

- In response, Christians in the sciences point to a wealth of evidence that the universe looks designed to produce the building blocks of life.

- The laws of physics "conspired" to ensure the universe would contain an abundance of hydrogen necessary for life.

- Three coincidences came about to ensure the right amount of carbon for life in the universe.

- The laws of physics take a form that not only permit the existence of life-essential elements (hydrogen, carbon, oxygen) but also drive their production, indicating that the universe is designed with a purpose.

Chapter 16

What Does the Bible Say about Life Out There?

Does the Bible say anything about extraterrestrial life? The short answer is "No." But, what the Bible *does* say reveals how God relates to humanity and raises other questions worth addressing.

What about Angels and Demons?
The Bible clearly states that humanity is not the only class of intelligent, self-aware creatures. A powerful, diabolical being tempted Adam and Eve in the Garden of Eden in order to draw the first couple away from proper relationship with God. An army of angels protected the prophet Elisha from the army of Syria (2 Kings 6:8–23). Satan, the most powerful created being also subjected Job to great trials and loss to tempt Job to reject God. The Gospels tell of demons that possess humans (Mark 1:23–27) and animals (Matthew 8:28–34). Matthew, Mark, Luke, and John also reveal that angels announce exciting news (Luke 1:8–38; John 20:11–13), minister to the tempted (Matthew 4:1–11), and were part of Jesus's teaching (John 1:51). The apostle Paul declares that neither angels nor demons can separate us from God's love (Romans 8:38–39) but demons can delay and hinder plans (1 Thessalonians 2:17–18). The last book of the Bible, Revelation, showcases the final battle between the angels and demons that results in the final judgment of all those (both human and angelic) who have rejected God. Angels and demons pervade the books of the Bible.

The description of angels and demons in the Bible tells us some important things. They are purely spiritual beings that have no physical bodies. In contrast, humans have both a physical and spiritual existence. Though angels have no physical existence, they can affect physical outcomes. The demon-possessed people encountered throughout the Bible can demonstrate extraordinary strength (Mark 5:1–4) or even knowledge of events that humans shouldn't know (Acts 16:16–19).

Two things are clear. While angels and demons can interact with the space-time dimensions of our universe, they do not live here. So, they do not qualify as extraterrestrial beings (because they have no physical bodies) that we might find by looking through our telescopes at some distant exoplanet. Second, members of the angelic realm (both angels and demons) possess intelligence and some capacity for free will (like humanity). However, once the angels decided to rebel against God's order, they had no chance for redemption (unlike humanity).

If Extraterrestrial Life Exists, Why Doesn't the Bible Tell Us?

Skeptics and believers alike want to know: Does the Bible definitively explain whether extraterrestrial life exists? To answer this question, we must first understand how Christianity thinks about God's revelation through Scripture. Throughout history Christians have largely agreed that the Bible speaks accurately on any topic it addresses. That does not mean that the Bible addresses every possible topic, nor does it comprehensively deal with every topic it addresses. So, Christians have no problem with electrons, quantum mechanics and general relativity, bacteria, or galaxies even though the biblical authors never wrote about any of these ideas. The authors never explicitly discussed ancient civilizations like the Incas, Chinese, and Aboriginal Australians even though these groups predate the final writings included in the New Testament.

From the very first pages of the Bible, God uses creation to give humanity a deeper understanding of how we relate to him. In Genesis 1, where God provides details of the physical creation, God instructs the first humans to "be fruitful and increase in number; fill the earth and subdue it. Rule over the fish in the sea and the birds in the sky and over every living creature that moves on the ground" (v. 28). Just a few verses later, when describing the creation from the perspective of how things are related, God instructs the first man (Adam) to name every creature. In doing this task, the man would understand his need for a suitable helper to fulfill his mission. Adam would realize his need for relationship with other humans and see how God met that need through the first woman (Eve). Stated simply, the Bible was never intended to give an exhaustive account of everything humanity would encounter. However, the Bible does give a complete description of everything humanity needs to know to have a right relationship with God.

Wouldn't Finding ET Diminish Humanity's Importance?

Many skeptics and Christians believe that finding extraterrestrial life (ET) would categorically diminish the importance of humanity. Paul Davies, an agnostic physicist at Arizona State University, wrote in *The Atlantic* that:

> The discovery of just a single bacterium somewhere beyond Earth would force us to revise our understanding of who we are and where we fit into the cosmic scheme of things, throwing us into a deep spiritual identity crisis that would be every bit as dramatic as the one Copernicus brought about in the early 1500s, when he asserted that Earth was not at the center of the universe.[1]

Gary Bates, leader in a prominent Christian ministry, puts it this way:

> We believe that sentient, intelligent, moral-decision-capable beings is [a threat to Christianity], because it would undermine the authority of Scripture. In short, understanding the big picture of the Bible/gospel message allows us to conclude clearly that the reason the Bible doesn't mention extraterrestrials (ETs) is that there aren't any. Surely, if the earth were to be favoured with a visitation by real extraterrestrials from a galaxy far, far away, then one would reasonably expect that the Bible, and God in His sovereignty and foreknowledge, to mention such a momentous occasion, because it would clearly redefine man's place in the universe.[2]

Both of these statements imply that humanity's significance relies on our unique existence in the universe.

Davies's comment misses a key feature of what makes humanity special. The Bible communicates that our special status rests in the fact that God made us in his image (Genesis 1:26–27). Although Scripture declares this truth, understanding exactly what it means requires great care, study, and reflection.[3] Even with a limited understanding, note that nothing about being created in God's image is reflected in our physical location, special timing, or uniqueness in creation. So, the fact that Earth is not the center of the solar system has absolutely no bearing on our importance.[4]

Bates's assertion rests on the premise that the main thrust of Scripture precludes the existence of any sentient, intelligent life beyond humans and angels. He essentially argues that finding ETs would not fit with how the Bible describes the extent of humanity's fall, the incarnation of Jesus Christ on Earth, and redemption being confined strictly to humanity. Bates articulates a reasonable case, one held by many Christians and closely aligned with historic Christian thought. However, as discussed in chapter 19, many respected Christian theologians come to a different conclusion based on their careful analysis of the Bible.

One thing Christian theologians seem to agree on is that humanity reflects God's image but not God's *entire* image. If so, why couldn't God create some other sentient, intelligent beings that reflected his image in a different way than humanity? Such a scenario would not impinge on God's sovereignty, his relationship with humanity, or humanity's significance.

Wouldn't ETs' Existence Wreak Havoc on the End Times?

One essential teaching of Christianity is that humanity will spend only a limited time on Earth. Eventually, an end time will arrive. The study of the end times (eschatology) reveals a few points upon which virtually all Christians agree: (1) Jesus Christ will return to Earth; (2) the dead will be resurrected; (3) all humanity will experience a final judgment; (4) every human will enter into the eternal state (believers into God's presence, nonbelievers into eternal separation from God); and (5) God will bring forth the new creation.[5] These all represent key features of Christian doctrine that, if changed, would also alter the Christian faith. So, how would the end times work if extraterrestrial life exists?

Some Christians object to the existence of ETs on the grounds that the end times for which *our* planet has been warned would subject (unfairly) these sentient, intelligent beings to judgment and time frames beyond their control. ChristianAnswers.net expressed the concern this way:

> If God had created intelligent life on other worlds, it is hard to imagine that their lives would be calibrated by the failures of Earth's inhabitants. It seems unlikely and unfair that their distant planets would be destroyed by God because of His plan for Earth. The implication of Scripture is that there are no other intelligent beings besides man, animals, and the angels.[6]

Personally, I find this objection odd. I see evidence that God fashioned a universe with finely tuned laws such that stars produce plenty of carbon and oxygen (without destroying all the hydrogen). Further, he orchestrated the process of changing Earth from a water world with no life or oxygen to a continent-rich planet teeming with a great diversity of life. If God created life on some other planet(s), is it not reasonable to assume that he calibrated the events in all these places (including Earth) to culminate at the same time? This objection seems problematic only if the development of the universe, Earth (and other exoplanets harboring life), and life itself happens outside of God's sovereign control. Of course, advocating that position (that anything happens outside of God's sovereign control) departs from the teaching of Scripture and rewrites much of historic Christian thought.

The Bottom Line

Most Christian theologians agree that the Bible is largely silent on the topic of the existence of ETs. Historically, Christians generally agreed that nothing in the Bible indicates that sentient, intelligent life exists anywhere but Earth. That does *not* mean that Scripture demands such a position. By speculating what scientists might find, given our best understanding, and examining how those finds might affect our interpretation of the Bible, we gain a deeper understanding of the central truths of Christianity and just how important humanity is to God. And it's just plain fascinating to think what else God might have done!

Allowing for that possibility, are there any parameters limiting what any life-form might look like? Are any of the sci-fi scenarios realistic? As we continue to probe into space, what does the science tell us to date?

 Takeaways ————————————————————

- The Bible doesn't care to answer every question that humans can conjure, including whether aliens exist, but it does give us everything we need to know about a right relationship with God.

- Some skeptics and Christians believe that the discovery of any kind of extraterrestrial life poses a threat to Christianity because it undermines humanity's place in the universe.

- Humans reflect God's image but not God's *entire* image; perhaps God created other sentient beings that reflect his image in different ways.

Chapter 17

What Kinds of Life Are Possible?

Sci-fi films, comics, and TV shows offer plenty of examples of humans encountering life from somewhere beyond our planet. In *Transformers*, elite military personnel join Optimus Prime and his alien robot cohorts to defend our planet against an attack by other villainous robots. In comics and elsewhere, Lois Lane meets Superman, a Krypton native who gains great powers from "Earth's yellow Sun." And in the *Star Trek* universe, the crew of the *Enterprise* faces Klingons, Q, and the Borg. Most examples of fictional extraterrestrials bear a striking resemblance to life on Earth, although they often possess vastly superior abilities. Some of the creatures resemble Earth's simpler life-forms, such as the alien amoeba known as "The Blob." With these fictional examples in mind, it's no wonder that we speculate what kinds of life scientists might find as they continue to explore the heavens.

The Picture of Life on Earth

Earth features an astounding array of life! The prevailing scientific narrative of life on Earth starts with an incredibly rare, and largely unexplained, event that occurred nearly four billion years ago. Somewhere on primordial Earth a mixture of nonliving molecules transformed into the first life-form. Scientists readily admit they do not have a good understanding of how this life-from-nonlife event took place, nonetheless they seem confident that it did. The fossil record on Earth shows that over the next four billion years an increasingly complex, diverse, and sophisticated jumble of life developed on the planet. For most of this period, microbial life dominated Earth's surface. Some of these bacteria transformed the planet in ways detectable from great distances (like photosynthetic bacteria), while others leave far more subtle signatures. A majority of scientists think that this microbial ET life exists scattered throughout the galaxy.

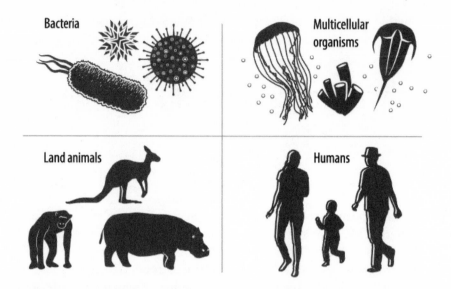

Figure 17.1: Known Possible Types of Life

Larger, multicellular animals appeared explosively just over 500 million years ago. The first of these animals lived exclusively in the water, with later versions showing up on land as well. Many animals exhibit a high degree of social behavior. Yet humanity alone represents the most advanced form of life on Earth. In addition to being highly relational, humans are the only creatures that question their place in the universe and actively try to gain knowledge that addresses that question.

If some form of relational ET or even sentient ET exists on some exoplanet out there, they would have a hard time finding us. For the bulk of human history, we made little in the way of a "signature" detectable beyond the confines of Earth. It would require technology far beyond our present abilities to detect humanity—even with our current level of civilization—from a distance. One key feature of humans (or of any sentient ET) is that they have a genuine history that informs what they see. Because we can imagine types of sentient life with no previous history (see "We Have No History," on page 147), let's use the term "ordinary observers" (OO) to refer to sentient life with an actual history.

What about the Multiverse?

Proponents of the multiverse often argue that its existence solves all the fine-tuning that life on Earth, particularly human life, requires. Chapter 10 addresses that question in more detail, but a few salient features warrant mention here. First, for the multiverse to adequately address the rarity of life on Earth, life must be completely physical. For example, if humans have a nonphysical, spiritual component as described in the Bible, no amount of rearranging the stuff of the universe would produce humans. Assuming that life is merely an improbable arrangement of atoms, the multiverse introduces at least three new types of life that are largely irrelevant in a single universe.

1. We Exist All Over the Place

The rarest hand in poker is a royal flush. In fact, for any given five-card hand, the chances of getting a royal flush of a specified suit are less than one in 2.5 million. However, dealing a billion hands virtually assures that a fairly large number of those hands will contain a royal flush of the specified suit. Additionally, every possible combination of cards exists in a large number of hands, meaning an even larger number of "almost" royal flushes (for example, having an ace of the wrong suit) also exist.[1]

In a level I multiverse, a large number of regions will look almost exactly like our observable universe. In one of those universes everything is the same except I decided not to write this book, or I decided to become a chemist instead of an astrophysicist, or my work in graduate school was rewarded with a Nobel Prize! In fact, any possible situation actually occurs in such a multiverse scenario. MIT cosmologist Max Tegmark calculated the distances to these "clone" regions and arrived at numbers like $10^{10^{29}}$ (10 to the 10 to the 29) meters away. Granted, these are huge distances but the clones come with a sufficiently large level I multiverse.

Inflation inevitably produces a sufficiently large multiverse such that many regions with ordinary observers (OOs) exist (assuming all life is purely physical); many that look exactly like what we see on Earth. The question becomes, will we ever discover OOs from other regions? For many people, such a scenario would diminish the importance of human life.

2. We Have No History

Despite the diversity of sci-fi extraterrestrials, few writers (again Douglas Adams is a notable exception) seem to deal with one of the most abundant forms of alien, the one that troubles cosmologists as they wrestle to understand the nature of the cosmos. That alien is the Boltzmann brain.

Most "normal" aliens have a history analogous to ours, a tangible past.

Boltzmann brains (BBs) do not because they arise from spontaneous fluctuations in the otherwise sterile vacuum of outer space. Although incredibly improbable (scientists use numbers like 1 in $10^{10^{16}}$ or 1 in $10^{10^{120}}$), thermodynamic fluctuations can transform the incredibly high entropy measured in space into a low entropy region occupied, for the briefest moment, by a sentient being. In a single, finite universe with a beginning 14 billion years ago, such infinitesimal probabilities mean that scientists can ignore the possibility of BBs. But the current cosmological models require a more careful treatment.

For example, in the distant future our universe will grow to enormous proportions. The vast size and incredible amount of time passed make BBs a real possibility. Add to this the existence of a multiverse and Boltzmann brain formation becomes almost certain. In such a scenario, two different "naturalistic" mechanisms exist for explaining life in the universe—the more familiar evolutionary molecules-to-man explanation (OOs) and the quantum/thermal fluctuations that lead to BBs (see page 147).

The key question given these two alternatives becomes which pathway produces the most typical form of life. In fact, most ways of comparing the life produced shows that BBs outnumber OOs. However, one must exercise caution because the cosmological models where these comparisons happen often involve universes that grow without bound, and that means scientists must find ways of counting and comparing infinite sets—a notoriously difficult task to accomplish. In fact, the simplest concepts of how to regulate the infinities (they go by names like "proper time cutoff," "stationary time," and "pocket-based measure"[2]) lead to predictions at odds with humanity appearing nearly 14 billion years after the creation of the universe.

3. We're a Simulation

Considering its box-office success, its safe to assume that most people are familiar with *The Matrix* trilogy. The series depicts a future in which most humans are enslaved in a computer-simulated reality known as the Matrix. Neo, the unwitting yet key player in the fight against the Matrix, meets Morpheus, leader of a band of free human rebels, who presents Neo with a choice: remain in the blissful ignorance of the Matrix simulation or escape to the gritty reality of the real world.

Alternate universes such as those in *The Matrix* may be things of fiction, but if the multiverse exists and if sufficiently complex simulations exist, then a fascinating scenario ensues. Simulated universes with simulated beings vastly outnumber any sentient life in "real," physical universes! Sir Martin Rees

Boltzmann brain   Computer simulation

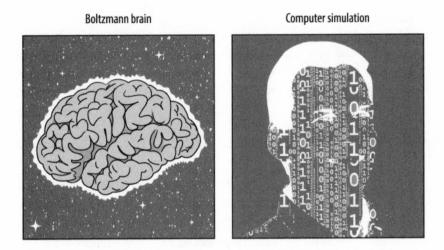

Figure 17.2: Speculative Types of Life—Boltzmann Brains and Simulations

explains this consequence of the multiverse:

> All these multiverse ideas lead to a remarkable synthesis between cosmology and physics. . . . But they also lead to the extraordinary consequence that we may not be the deepest reality, we may be a simulation. The possibility that we are creations of some supreme or super-being, blurs the boundary between physics and idealist philosophy, between the natural and the supernatural, and between the relation of mind and multiverse and the possibility that we're in the matrix rather than the physics itself.[3]

The Bottom Line

In a single universe, scientists need only concern themselves with explaining how this improbable sequence of events leading to humanity occurred. However, if a multiverse exists, then many other options for life need consideration. If life just requires the proper arrangement of atoms, then life abounds in the multiverse. Now we must answer questions like: Are we one of a bunch of copies? Are we simulations? Are we Boltzmann brains? Answering "Yes" to any of these would radically alter what we think of humanity's place in the cosmos.

Speaking of humanity, the farther out we look with scientific instruments, the smaller everything here seems. It would be natural to assume that humans take on less importance in the vastness of the cosmos. Earth is a speck; humans nearly invisible and very recent arrivals on that speck. Why would a Creator wait so long to make all of this in anticipation for one species? We'll dive into this question in the next chapter.

 Takeaways

- Earth's astounding array of life has gone largely unexplained from a naturalistic perspective.

- The multiverse solves fine-tuning problems for life on Earth and introduces three new categories or phases as part of the solution.

- Our universe's vast size (assuming a level I multiverse) and time available in the future make Boltzmann brain formation almost certain.

- If a multiverse exists, then many other options for life need consideration.

Chapter 18

Why Did God Wait So Long to Create Humans?

The universe started with a bang nearly 14 billion years ago. The solar system formed 4.5 billion years ago. Even the continents have been around for a couple billion years, and the first life-forms along with them. But when it comes to humanity and our arrival about 100,000 years ago, we are extreme latecomers to the creation story. If, as Christians claim, humanity is so important to God, why did he wait so long to create the first people?

This question has multiple facets, depending on the person asking. Skeptics usually argue that humanity is not central to anything.[1] Instead, people represent the most recent event in a series of purely naturalistic processes (that presumably will continue long after our death). Young-earth creationists (YECs) usually argue that such long periods of time are inconsistent with God's character and therefore didn't occur.[2]

Old-earth creationists accept a billions-of-years old universe. So, how do billions of years fit within a context where humanity plays a central role in God's creation?

Understanding God's Physical Laws

It is important to remember that if the God of the Bible exists, then his sovereign nature and his character set the standards and rules. God reveals through the Bible that he upholds and sustains the universe so reliably (see Jeremiah 33:25–26, for example) that we can describe the processes at work using the laws of physics. This reality brings two consequences. First, as a Christian and a scientist, my job is to study the universe to understand the way God upholds and sustains creation. I do not get to determine ahead of time what God should have done. Instead, I am supposed to seek comprehension of what he did. Second, the reliability of the laws of physics should provide insight regarding why God waited billions of years to create humans. So, do those laws tell us why humanity didn't appear until after nearly 14 billion years passed?

The Building Blocks of Life

One second after the universe started, it consisted of an incredibly hot (>1,000,000,000°F), incredibly dense soup of protons, neutrons, and energy. Over the next few minutes, it expanded and cooled such that some of the protons and neutrons fused into helium. At this time the composition (by mass) of the universe was 75% hydrogen, 25% helium, and a tiny fraction of a percent lithium and beryllium. However, even the most primitive kind of life needs a far more diverse suite of elements to exist. Let's just focus on the three most crittical—hydrogen, carbon, and oxygen. Carbon is the only element capable of providing the chemical complexity that life requires. Oxygen is a necessary component of water (along with hydrogen) as well as an element that provides a chemical energy reservoir multicellular life needs. Thanks to the lack of stable 5- and 8-nucleon elements (see chapter 15), the universe proceeded with an abundant supply of hydrogen. The synthesis of carbon and oxygen required the formation of stars.

Producing Enough Carbon and Oxygen

As discussed in chapter 15, the laws of physics are tuned to produce carbon and oxygen. In fact, changing the masses of the lightest two quarks by as little as 3% would result in a universe containing negligible amounts of carbon and oxygen. However, just because the universe *can* produce these two elements does not mean that it *will* produce them, or that the universe will do so quickly. In fact, it takes a few billion years for carbon and oxygen to form. Here's why.

Within an hour after the birth of the universe, the expansion rate dropped its temperature sufficiently low enough that no new elements could form. This makes sense when you consider that fusing lighter nuclei (like helium) together to form a heavier nucleus (like carbon) requires bringing the protons of each nucleus into close proximity. Because all protons have positive charge and like charges repel, it takes an enormous amount of energy to overcome this repulsion. At high enough temperatures, the nuclei have enough energy. Also, in a continuously expanding universe, the temperature steadily drops. If expansion were the only dynamic process in the universe, then nothing more than helium and hydrogen would exist. Fortunately, as the universe cools, the uniformly distributed mix of hydrogen and helium begins to fragment into clouds that start to collapse under their own gravity. The interiors of these collapsing clouds eventually heat up to the point where fusion occurs and stars are born.

The first phases of these stars result in more hydrogen fusing into helium because that occurs at the lowest temperature.

As hydrogen continues to fuse, helium builds up in the star's core. When the core exhausts all its hydrogen (roughly 10 billion years for stars as massive as the Sun), the core starts to contract and get hotter. Eventually, the temperature reaches the point where helium fuses into carbon and the core stops contracting—at least until it exhausts all its helium (100 million years). For stars like the Sun, making carbon takes a long time, although larger stars get through the carbon-producing phase much more quickly (~1 million years for the most massive stars).

Carbon locked in the interior of stars provides little benefit for life, though. Some process(es) must liberate the carbon back into the stuff that will make future stars. Stars more than eight times the mass of the Sun eventually exhaust all fuel sources for fusion, causing the star to rapidly collapse.[3] A supernova (the explosion that happens as the collapsing material rebounds off the dense iron core) disperses the star's material back into the galaxy for use in the next generation of stars. The energy given off during a supernova often exceeds the brightness of an entire galaxy.

Stars similar in mass to the Sun (roughly half to ten times) eject material in a different fashion. After the star exhausts the hydrogen and helium in the core, it expands tremendously—enough to engulf the orbit of Earth! At this point the internal structure consists of a core made of carbon and oxygen surrounded by a shell where helium still fuses to carbon and another shell where hydrogen fuses to helium (see figure 18.1). Though the hydrogen shell is relatively stable, the helium shell exhibits great variability that dredges up material from the core, mixes it throughout the star, and even ejects the outer layers of the star. Stars in this phase may lose up to 70% of their mass for incorporation into future stars.

The first stars formed around 200 million years after the start of the universe. The explosion of these massive first stars introduced the carbon and oxygen into future star-forming material for the first time. Since then, the abundance of carbon and oxygen has grown as more stars go supernova and as smaller stars lose their outer layers. And here is why all of this discussion and detail seem to matter. Life on Earth requires a sufficient supply of carbon and oxygen. Perhaps it takes nearly 9 billion years for a galaxy like ours to acquire the necessary supply.

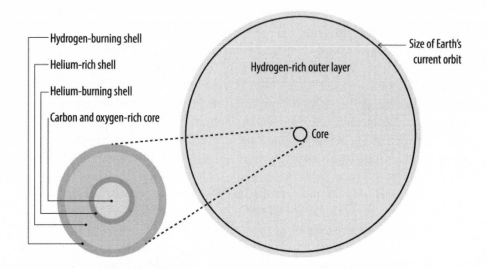

Hydrogen-burning shell

Helium-rich shell

Helium-burning shell

Carbon and oxygen-rich core

Hydrogen-rich outer layer

Size of Earth's current orbit

Core

Figure 18.1: The Future of the Sun (and Other Stars with Similar Mass)
Astronomers call these asymptotic giant branch (AGB) stars.

Free Oxygen in the Atmosphere

Humanity and all other large-bodied organisms require an abundance of oxygen in the atmosphere to live. Handily, oxygen makes up 21% of the atmosphere. However, throughout much of Earth's history the atmosphere had either no free oxygen or a small fraction of today's value. The early Earth started with no oxygen in its atmosphere, a condition that persisted for the next 2 billion years. Some scientific details are still fuzzy, but about 2.5 billion years ago oxygen became a permanent component of the atmosphere—although at only a few percent of present levels.

Consider a sink with the faucet turned on. Water from the faucet fills the sink, but the drain removes water from the sink. In order to fill the sink with water, the flow from the faucet must exceed the rate going down the drain (either by opening the faucet further or putting a towel over the drain). This picture illustrates the level of oxygen in the atmosphere. Organisms called cyanobacteria produce oxygen through photosynthesis, but free oxygen readily reacts to combine with other compounds. Around 2.5 billion years ago, the abundance of cyanobacteria grew or some geological change reduced the amount of oxygen-reacting material (or both happened), because oxygen started filling the atmosphere.

The oxygen concentration remained relatively constant for the next two billion years, and single-celled life continued to dominate instead of more advanced multicellular life. A team of scientists identified one possible explanation for this long delay despite the initial rapid jump in atmospheric oxygen.[4]

Many of the more complex single-celled organisms and most of the multicellular ones must transform the abundant nitrogen in the atmosphere into a more usable form—a process referred to as "nitrogen fixation." In order to fix nitrogen efficiently, certain bacteria need sufficient quantities of the element molybdenum. Yet the scientists found that the oceans contained far less molybdenum compared to current values until roughly 600 million years ago when the first multicellular animals explosively appeared in the fossil record.

The main source of oceanic molybdenum derives from weathering of continental crust in the presence of abundant oxygen. Thus, it appears that during the two-billion-year period after the first oxidation event, both geological and biological processes were transforming Earth's atmosphere and oceans from an oxygen-poor, molybdenum-poor condition to one with growing supplies of both elements.

Just as builders pour the concrete foundation before framing the walls, this transformation prepared Earth for the rapid and widespread introduction of complex, multicellular animals during the Avalon and Cambrian explosions. However, one critical step remained—the atmosphere needed more oxygen.

Studies of the Doushantuo Formation in the Yangtze River's Three Gorges area of South China contain abundant fossils formed between 635 and 551 million years ago—the time period just prior to the Cambrian explosion. Analysis of carbon isotopes throughout the formation revealed that two additional oxidation events occurred during the period when it was deposited.[5]

These events raised the oxygen content of the atmosphere above 60% of present levels and also fully oxygenated the oceans. In particular, the researchers noted that the first pulse of oxygen resulted in a rise in microscopic organisms, and a second pulse coincides with a dramatic increase in large, complex algae. In each case, the number of species present in the fossil formations doubled. Furthermore, in the 15 million years following the second pulse, complex macroscopic life-forms, dubbed Ediacaran organisms, increased dramatically worldwide.

Earth's Remarkable Magnetic Field

In addition to a planet containing enough carbon, free oxygen, and organisms

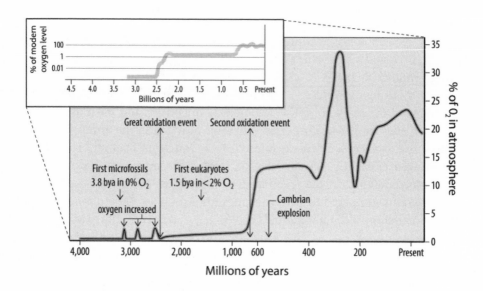

Figure 18.2: The Changing Amount of Oxygen in Earth's Atmosphere
Notice the two distinct epochs when the concentration of oxygen increased dramatically as shown in the upper left insert.

that can fix nitrogen, complex, multicellular organisms also require a planet with a stable, long-lasting magnetic field.

Research indicates that Earth has had a strong magnetic field for much of its existence, but not the strong dipole character seen today (north and south poles closely aligned with the rotation axis). Recent studies indicate some significant changes in the strength and configuration during the last 2 billion years. Around 1.7 billion years ago, the magnetic field transitioned from a configuration with multiple poles to a dipole. Then 1 billion years ago, the field weakened and the poles became highly variable. Finally, 650 million years ago, right before the Cambrian explosion, when abundant and diverse multicellular organisms appeared on Earth, it transitioned to the current strong dipole configuration.[6] Furthermore, it appears that the transition back to the strong dipole regime may coincide with the formation of a solid inner core.

Such variable and complex magnetic field configurations before 650 million years ago had little effect on life because, at that time, it resided almost exclusively in the water. After the Cambrian explosion, life appeared on the continents. Until the nucleation of the inner core occurred, Earth's magnetic field would exhibit too much variability in strength and direction to provide the shielding that advanced, complex life like humans require.

Is Humanity Important?

So, can humanity be of central importance in the context of a 14-billion-year-old universe? Yes! Given the laws of physics God chose to govern the cosmos, it took 9 billion years to form a planet capable of supporting life and 4.5 billion years to prepare that planet to host humans. As to why God "waited" so long, that involves more of a theological discussion about God's relationship to time. For our purposes in this book, billions of years is an eyeblink to God.

Still, not everyone agrees that Earth represents the only planet capable of supporting human life, but the next few decades of exoplanet exploration will provide a wealth of data that will help answer this question more definitively. For now, we turn our attention to *the key question* for many people. If Christianity is to remain true in this age of discovery, do we need Jesus to be some kind of planet-hopping Savior?

 Takeaways ――――――――――――――――――――――――――――

- We lack understanding of God's sovereign ways, but the reliability of the laws of physics should provide insight regarding why God waited billions of years to create humanity.

- Humanity and all other large-bodied organisms require an abundance of oxygen in the atmosphere (21%) to live, and it took 9 billion years of fine-tuning to get it.

- Geological and biological processes transformed Earth's atmosphere and oceans from oxygen-poor and molybdenum-poor to one with growing supplies of both elements, which were key to complex life during the Avalon and Cambrian explosions.

- Earth's strong, dipole magnetic field and solid inner core coincided with the rise of multicellular organisms.

- Given the laws of phyics that brought about the cosmos, it took 9 billion years to form a planet capable of supporting life and another 4.5 billion years to set the stage for human arrival.

- In that sense, yes, humanity is important.

Chapter 19

Would the Discovery of ET Disprove Christianity?

According to popular narrative, Copernicus's assertion that Earth orbited the Sun started a relentless process of scientific discovery serving to remove any thought that humanity occupied a special place in the universe. Earth was not the center of the solar system, the Sun was not the center of the galaxy, and the Milky Way Galaxy was not the center of the universe. Many people take this idea even further to claim that Earth, including the life inhabiting it, is completely mediocre in every way. The discovery of any kind of life—especially intelligent life—beyond the confines of Earth would forever falsify the notion that humanity has any claim of exceptionalism.

Associated with this line of reasoning, many believe that discovery of extraterrestrial (ET) life would powerfully demonstrate that many of the world's religions, particularly Christianity, cannot be true. After all, the Bible mentions nothing about life beyond Earth! So, would the discovery of ET disprove Christianity? It's possible, but not likely.

Essentials of Christianity

Before evaluating the effect on Christianity of finding ET, one must understand the foundation of the Christian faith. Unless finding ET undermines the basis of Christianity or directly contradicts a teaching of the Bible, the hypothetical discovery cannot disprove the faith. So, what are the basics of the Christian faith?

Creation, Fall, Incarnation, Resurrection, and New Creation

Throughout history, Christians have sought to articulate the essential beliefs of the faith. The carefully chosen wording of the Apostles' Creed summarizes them in this way:

> I believe in God, the Father almighty, *creator of heaven and earth.* I believe in Jesus Christ, God's only Son, our Lord, who was *conceived by the Holy Spirit, born of the Virgin Mary,* suffered under Pontius Pilate, was crucified, died, and was buried; he descended to the dead. On the third day *he rose again;* he ascended into heaven, he is seated at the right hand of the Father, and he will come to judge the living and the dead. I believe in the Holy Spirit, the holy catholic Church, the communion of saints, the forgiveness of sins, *the resurrection of the body, and the life everlasting.* Amen. (emphasis added)[1]

Creation. Genesis 1:1 declares "In the beginning God created the heavens and the earth." The Hebrew word for created, *bara,* carries the connotation that God brought the universe into existence out of nothing (creation *ex nihilo*). In other words, God is the maker of the universe. He determines how the universe operates, decides how to reveal himself to humanity, provides the standard of right and wrong, and judges the standing of each human. One primary function of the Bible is to communicate God's revelation of himself to humanity, particularly how we relate to him. Because we are the creation and God is the Creator, our role is to submit our actions to his direction.

The Fall. After God created the universe and fashioned Earth as a habitat for humanity, he created the first humans, Adam and Eve, and placed them in the Garden of Eden. One of the couple's first recorded acts was to disobey God's command and eat of the forbidden tree. God is just; hence, their rebellion required judgment. Adam and Eve served as humanity's representatives in the Garden and rejected God's command, resulting in humanity's eternal separation from God.

The Incarnation. Though God is just, he is also compassionate. The only option for humanity after Adam and Eve's sin was eternal separation. However, God chose to reveal himself in an incredible way. Jesus, the second person of the Trinity, came to Earth as a man. He did not cease to be God (that would violate the character of God as well as the rules of logic) but took on a human nature. In theological terms, Jesus was fully God *and* fully man in hypostatic union. As a human being without sin, he could bear the punishment for sin required by God's justice.

The Resurrection. Two millennia ago, when Jesus Christ walked the earth as a man, his life ended in a brutal crucifixion. His sinless life enabled his death on the cross to atone for the sin of humanity. However, the story does not end there. On the third day, Jesus rose from the dead, validating the biblical claim that he was God.

The New Creation. Jesus commissioned his followers to go to the ends of the earth so that everyone can know how God redeemed humanity from its rebellion. All who receive Christ's atonement by faith become part of God's kingdom. Eventually, Christ will return to Earth and usher all who belong in his kingdom into a new creation. All who refuse Christ's atoning work on the cross will spend eternity apart from God (the logical outcome of their choice), enduring life devoid of all the goodness, blessing, and fulfillment God's presence brings. Obviously, this brief description of five doctrines taken from the Apostles' Creed does not explain the entire Christian faith. Whole books are needed for that task.

One of the Bible's primary functions is to reveal this message of redemption to all humanity. Sin leaves every person on this planet condemned before a holy, righteous God. Only the sacrifice of his perfect Son can pay our debt and satisfy his justice. Faith is the gift he gives so we can be reconciled to him. Would finding life beyond the confines of Earth contradict any aspect of this redemption message?

How Would ET Affect Christianity?

The type of ET found influences the answer. Few, if any, theologians would have any concerns about finding microbial life on a distant exoplanet. From a theological perspective, the Bible makes no explicit claims about the origin of life. However, Genesis 1:2 may imply that God created life early in Earth's history and then protected it during an era when conditions on the planet were hostile for any living thing. A discovery of microbial ET would raise questions regarding life's origin and whether it requires anything beyond the normal operation of the physical laws governing our universe. It may be that God created a universe where life arises by naturalistic processes, but one can make a strong case based on our best scientific understanding that life's origin and the development of Earth's life-friendly conditions both require divine intervention.[2]

Microbial ET represents the more likely find, but discovering intelligent ET would be *far more* theologically compelling (like humanity that is "made in God's image"). The Bible is largely silent on the issue of intelligent ET (at least the physical kind), so the dominant position in historic Christian thought is that humanity represents the only intelligent physical life in the universe. Just as people have speculated on the existence of intelligent ET for centuries, theologians have also contemplated how such a finding would interact with historic Christian thought.[3] Here are some of the proposals offered, in no particular order. All of these options, except for the last one, assume that God created intelligent life on other worlds and that these creatures, like humanity, chose to rebel against God.

1. Jesus's incarnation, death, and resurrection here on Earth was a singularly important happening that results in redemption for *all* intelligent ET. Perhaps humanity will spread throughout the universe, taking the gospel to all these creatures. Or maybe God reveals himself on each of these planets in a way that declares what Jesus accomplished on Earth. This option does present at least one difficulty. The Bible describes Jesus as the second Adam, meaning that both are related physically and in nature. Any intelligent ETs in this scenario have no physical relation (and maybe not even in nature) to Jesus.

2. Jesus becomes incarnate on each planet where creatures rebel, taking on the nature of the beings, created by God, on each planet. Although God created humanity in his image, perhaps his creations on other planets have a nature that reflects God's image in different ways. Given the description of the hypostatic union offered by Thomas Aquinas, the addition of *other* natures besides Jesus's human one seems plausible.

3. The nature of the rebellion of other intelligent ETs requires another means of redemption for them. Given that God has only revealed the redemption plan for humanity, any proposals for what these other redemption paths look like are pure speculation.

4. No redemption is possible. This option seems the most offensive to human sensibilities, specifically because of the difficulty of reconciling it with God's goodness, omniscience, and power. Some would object that an all-knowing, all-good, all-powerful God cannot create beings subject to eternal hell. In fact, many raise the same objection in the context of humanity. However, a few points warrant mention. First, our finite minds cannot comprehend all that God knows. Second, true free will has consequences. While God is good in his nature, he is also just. Although this option seems offensive, it does have precedent in the Bible. Angels had a choice to either serve God or Lucifer. No offer of redemption exists for those angels who followed Lucifer.

5. God created intelligent life with free will, but these creatures chose not to rebel as humans did. Lacking any violation of God's command, these creatures have no need of redemption. They already enjoy proper relationship with God. C. S. Lewis explores this idea in his Space Trilogy.

One final, and very real, possibility: God created only one intelligent creature in the entire universe. If so, then the redemption story of life on Earth is *the story* of the universe and this discussion becomes moot.

Science and Theology's Common Ground

A common objection scientists level against Christianity, and religion in general, is its apparent lack of testability. Stated another way, they charge that Christianity is so flexible and vague that nothing could ever falsify it. Ironically, many people (Christians and non-Christians alike) think that finding intelligent ET would falsify Christianity. The discussion on page 162 identifies a number of ways that historic Christian theology would incorporate the discovery of intelligent ET. But doesn't the wide number of options just validate the charge of inordinate flexibility and vagueness?

Actually, scientists deem that property a virtue. Consider a topic investigated extensively by the scientific community over the last hundred years: What is the proper interpretation of quantum mechanics? One might think this to be a settled question, considering that quantum mechanics is one of the two most successful scientific models ever developed (the other is general relativity). A quick perusal of the literature reveals that many different interpretations exist for the underlying nature of quantum mechanics.[4] The breadth of options on this topic represents the outstanding efforts of many scientists to address a difficult question. Developing a range of interpretations helps scientists know the experiments that will distinguish which interpretation best represents reality. Similarly, a range of models for ET's redemption helps theologians discern underlying details of God's redemptive story.

Einstein's development of his theory of relativity did not prove Newton wrong. Newtonian dynamics still describes properly the motion of the vast majority of objects through space. Einstein's relativity just gives a more complete picture of how gravity operates. If we find intelligent ET (and that's a *big if*), the discovery would not invalidate the historic Christian understanding of redemption. Like Einstein's relativity, the discovery of intelligent ET would give us a more complete picture of how God interacts with humanity. Jesus's life, death, and resurrection still provides the only means of redemption for fallen humans, but maybe God's redemption narrative encompasses more than just humanity.

The search goes on. We still have not fully answered one question: Do we have neighbors of some kind or another out there? We address that question in the final chapter.

Takeaways ———————————————————————————————

- Unless finding ET undermines the foundation of the Christian faith in some way, its hypothetical discovery cannot disprove the faith.

- Christianity has historically confessed several foundational truths that have withstood the test of time; these include creation, the fall, the incarnation, the resurrection, and the eternal state.

- One of the Bible's primary functions is to reveal the message of redemption to all humanity; thus, the idea that finding life anywhere else would contradict this message seems unlikely.

- Microbial ET seems a more likely find, but the Bible is largely silent on the existence of intelligent ET, though theologians have speculated on how to account for them in five ways.

- If scientists discover intelligent life, the finding would not invalidate the historic Christian faith but will provide a more complete picture of God's creation.

Chapter 20

Must ET Exist?

In a digital age we have grown accustomed to the accelerated pace of discoveries. For many people, science, engineering, and medical breakthroughs have provided and will continue to provide answers to all of humanity's challenges—thus, it will be no different here. Science will ultimately answer the question, "Is there life out there?"

But it hasn't. And for those like me who want a definitive answer, it will likely be decades before we have any data that directly addresses the issue.

An Argument in Favor of ET

Consider a photon (something like a particle of light) emitted in the early history of the universe. When the universe was just 400,000 years old, it cooled to a temperature where protons and electrons could form hydrogen atoms. Every electron that joined a proton emitted one photon of light somewhere in the visible-to-infrared range of the electromagnetic spectrum. As this photon traveled toward the location where Earth would eventually orbit, its odyssey was marked by nearly unfathomable distances and wonders.

About 200 million years later, the photon encountered the first stars to form in the universe. Scientists have not yet found the light emitted by these stars, but calculations show that they were likely giants by today's standards. These first stars had masses tens and even hundreds of times larger than our Sun. Consequently, some of them burned through their nuclear fuel in just a few million years before exploding in spectacular supernovae. The energy emitted by these stars kicked all the electrons away from their protons, thus reionizing the universe.

As the photon continued its journey, it passed the first galaxies. Often these galaxies hosted an incredibly large black hole at their centers. The largest black holes measured to date weigh in at a staggering 30–40 billion times the mass of the Sun. For comparison, the Milky Way Galaxy (MWG) hosts a black hole with a mere 4.3 million solar masses. During the early history of the universe, many of these massive black holes consumed large amounts of dust and stars and emitted copious amounts of X-rays and gamma rays.

Over the next 10–12 billion years, the photon passed galaxy clusters so large that it would take over 500 million years to traverse them—and that's traveling at the speed of light! Eventually, the photon would enter a relatively small group of galaxies (on the outskirts of a 100,000-galaxy supercluster) containing our home, the MWG. Even after entering the MWG, the photon still had tens of thousands of years before it would approach the Sun. Along this last segment of the journey, it encountered even more bizarre conditions. Some of the stars exploded as supernovae that scatter the elements critical to life throughout the galaxy. Others, called neutron stars, are more massive than the Sun but so dense that their sizes are similar to a large US city. These neutron stars spin on their axis at rates exceeding 30 times a second and emit beams of harsh X-rays and gamma rays (just like the massive black holes, but closer to home).

Beyond the bizarre stars, the photon also encountered a myriad of "normal" stars. These range in mass from a few tenths of the Sun up to a few tens of the Sun. The more massive stars burn for a few million years, but the least massive burn for trillions of years!

When this photon finally reached Earth nearly 14 billion years later, more than 95% of all stars that will ever form already existed.[1] In just the MWG, hundreds of billions of Earth-sized planets exist around these stars. The photon changed significantly because space was expanding during the entire journey. The original wavelength near visible light has stretched to microwaves. Furthermore, the location where the photon originated now sits almost 50 billion light-years away! We live in a truly gargantuan universe that has grown and developed for a tremendous amount of time.

When considering the staggering size and age of the universe, many people conclude that life must exist out there. That idea was voiced strongly during the movie *Contact* (1997). The closing scene involves a dialogue between the protagonist Dr. Ellie Arroway and a group of children taking a tour of the Very Large Array (nobody ever said scientists used creative names). In response to a child who asks if there are other people out there in the universe, Ellie says:

> The most important thing is that you all keep searching for your own answers. I'll tell you one thing about the universe, though. The universe is a pretty big place. It's bigger than anything anyone has

ever dreamed of before. So, if it's just us, it seems like an awful waste of space.[2]

This assertion resonates with a large number of people. Examining life here on Earth adds weight to the argument. Life abounds on our home planet! Animals fill almost every conceivable niche available—from deserts to mountains, from the surface to the depths of the oceans, from sea level to high mountains, and almost everywhere in between. The smaller the life, the more varied the environments they inhabit. Scientists have discovered bacterial life that flourishes in temperatures both above the boiling point and below the freezing point of water. Other organisms grow optimally in highly basic or highly acidic conditions. Others still thrive in high-radiation environments, extremely dry conditions, or situations with high concentrations of metals, salt, or sugar. Life exists in every possible environment—even in some that scientists once thought impossible!

One final fact to buttress the claim that life exists out there is that life appeared on Earth almost as soon as the planet could support it. As my colleague Dr. Fazale Rana points out in his book *Origins of Life*, the fossil record shows life at 3.5 billion years and the geochemical record indicates life as far back as 3.8+ billion years.[3] Considering that asteroids and comets pummeled Earth until about 3.9 billion years ago, life appeared in a geological instant—as soon as Earth could possibly host it.

Might Earth Be the Only Planet to Host Life?

Life requires elements that permit complex biochemical reactions. As described in chapter 6, carbon seems uniquely suited to fulfill this role. Additionally, chapter 4 explains why water serves as the ideal solvent for carbon chemistry. As scientists determined how these elements (carbon, oxygen, and hydrogen) formed in the universe, they discovered that slight changes in the laws of physics would lead to a universe devoid of these building blocks. Yet, they also recognize that the laws of physics produced them in abundance. In this way, our universe seems rather "friendly" to life. Even more so considering that most, if not all, stars host an assortment of planets. But why, if our universe were so friendly to life's building blocks, would one argue that only Earth harbors life?

Carbon, liquid water, and planets are necessary components for life. However, investigations of the planets in our solar system demonstrate that these components are not sufficient to produce life. Studies of Mars show an abundance of evidence for liquid water in the past and transient periods of water more recently. In fact, one set of images revealed two massive debris fields likely caused by tsunamis roughly 3.5 billion years ago.[4] Any liquid water on Mars has long since disappeared,[5] but the ancient ocean required for any tsunami to form might have contained some form of microbial life. Given the minimal atmosphere on Mars, the chemical and radiation environment on the planet would quickly destroy any past or present biological material.[6] The strong evidence of water on Mars in the past provides scientists with a promising opportunity—the chance to study, in far more detail than any exoplanet, the possibility that Mars actually hosted life.

Perhaps probes sent to Mars in the not-too-distant future could excavate the tsunami debris fields and test for any extant or extinct life from the ancient shoreline. Similar opportunities exist with Enceladus and Europa. These moons of Saturn and Jupiter, although they are covered by miles-thick layers of ice, also show strong evidence of liquid water. Maybe future missions could collect the water (as it occasionally escapes from cracks in the ice) and test it for signs of current or past life. If detailed studies of the known liquid water environments in the solar system show no evidence of life, these results would lend credence to the idea that life is a rare phenomenon in the universe.[7]

A growing body of evidence indicates that Earth's remarkable capacity to host a thriving and diverse array of life requires far more than liquid water. Perhaps any habitable planet requires an uncommon migration of planets during the early period of formation, a suitable size for ongoing plate tectonic activity, a just-right sized moon, a suitably dynamic atmosphere that adjusts to the changing brightness of the Sun, and many other characteristics. If so, maybe the odds of a truly habitable planet dwarf the number of planets available. Given these possibilities, Earth may be the *only* planet containing life in the observable universe.

It's an Open Question

Scientifically speaking, the existence of intelligent, sentient life beyond the confines of Earth is an open question. As I survey the scientific landscape, I find that the best explanation for all we see is that the God of the Bible created a universe capable of supporting life, prepared a planet to harbor advanced life, and then created humanity on that planet. The fine-tuned nature of the laws of physics, the purposeful events that could have destroyed Earth but enhanced its ability to support life, and the capacity of humans to understand it all point to something outside of the physical universe that orchestrated the whole story. That said, *I think the existence of life beyond Earth is also an open theological question.*

If God created life here on Earth, why couldn't he have done it somewhere else also?

Let's continue to explore the heavens, searching for distant planets, while developing the technology to determine if life inhabits these remote worlds. I can't help but echo the words of Ellie Arroway when a special committee presses her to provide evidence of her encounter with ETs.

> I can't prove it, I can't even explain it, but everything that I know as a human being, everything that I am tells me that it was real! I was given something wonderful, something that changed me forever. A vision of the universe that tells us, undeniably, how tiny and insignificant and how rare and precious we all are! A vision that tells us that we belong to something that is greater than ourselves, that we are *not*, that none of us are alone! I wish I could share that. I wish that everyone, if even for one moment, could feel that awe and humility and hope.[8]

Ellie Arroway contends that discovering ETs will bring hope, vision, and purpose. My wish is that as you examine the heavens and see the wonder and majesty of creation, you come to know that we are not alone in the universe. The Creator, who revealed himself in Jesus Christ, fashioned this universe so that we could have a relationship with him. Indeed, we are not alone and that brings true awe, humility, and hope.

Notes

Introduction: The Quest to Find Our Place in the Universe

1. Michael J. Crowe, ed., *The Extraterrestrial Life Debate, Antiquity to 1915: A Source Book* (Notre Dame: University of Notre Dame Press, 2008), xvi.
2. Ibid., 52.
3. Ibid., 60–61.
4. Dennis R. Danielson, "The Great Copernican Cliché," *American Journal of Physics* 69 (October 2001): 1029–35, doi:10.1119/1.1379734.
5. Crowe, *Extraterrestrial Life Debate*, 27.
6. For a good sampling of those reasons, see Stephen Webb, *If the Universe Is Teeming with Aliens . . . Where Is Everybody?* (New York: Copernicus Books, 2002).
7. For the explanation of this equation from the organization founded by Frank Drake, see "The Drake Equation," SETI Institute, accessed April 25, 2017, http://www.seti.org/node/434.
8. Michel Mayor and Didier Queloz, "A Jupiter-Mass Companion to a Solar-Type Star," *Nature* 378 (November 1995): 355–59, doi:10.1038/378355a0.
9. Officially, in 1992 astronomers found a system of two or more planets orbiting the pulsar PSR 1257+12 (now called PSR B1257+12). See A. Wolszczan and D. A. Frail, "A Planetary System around the Millisecond Pulsar PSR 1257+12," *Nature* 355 (January 1992): 145–47, doi:10.1038/355145a0. Pulsars are embers of dead stars that happen to spin very rapidly—160 times per second in this instance. However, I am concerned with the search for potential life sites, so I am restricting the discussion to planets orbiting stars that are still in the hydrogen-burning phase of their lives. Astronomers refer to these as main sequence stars.
10. Arthur C. Clarke, *The Star*, Internet Archive, http://web.archive.org/

web/20080718084442/http://lucis.net/stuff/clarke/star_clarke.html, accessed March 6, 2017.

Chapter 1: The Big Picture

1. The current best measurements in the scientific literature date the universe between 13.76 and 13.85 billion years. I've chosen to round this date to 14 billion years for readability's sake.

2. You might wonder how the *observable* universe can be 46 billion light-years across but only 14 billion light-years old. The short answer is that the light from the most distant regions was emitted shortly after the beginning of the universe, but the universe has expanded dramatically as that light made its way to Earth.

3. Obviously we don't have direct evidence for this giant impact model, but it is by far the best explanation for the present Earth-Moon system.

4. For example, see A. I. S. Kemp et al., "Episodic Growth of the Gondwana Supercontinent from Hafnium and Oxygen Isotopes in Zircon," *Nature* 439 (February 2006): 580–83, doi:10.1038/nature04505; and D. G. Pearson, S. W. Parman, and G. M. Nowell, "A Link between Large Mantle Melting Events and Continent Growth Seen in Osmium Isotopes," *Nature* 449 (September 2007): 202–5, doi:10.1038/nature06122.

5. For more on how the record of nature affirms the creation account, see Hugh Ross, *Genesis One: A Scientific Perspective* (Glendora, CA: Reasons to Believe, 2006).

Chapter 2: What Would a Day on Another Planet Look Like?

1. A. Wolszczan and D. A. Frail, "A Planetary System around the Millisecond Pulsar PSR 1257+12," Nature 355 (January 1992): 145–47, doi:10.1038/355145a0.

2. Michel Mayor and Didier Queloz, "A Jupiter-Mass Companion to a Solar-Type Star," *Nature* 378 (November 1995): 355–59, doi:10.1038/378355a0; Geoffrey W. Marcy et al., "The Planet around 51 Pegasi," *Astrophysical Journal* 481 (June 1997): 926–35, doi:10.1086/304088.

3. William D. Cochran et al., "The Discovery of a Planetary Companion to 16 Cygni B," *Astrophysical Journal* 483 (July 1997): 457–63, doi:10.1086/304245.

4. Laurance R. Doyle et al., "Kepler-16: A Transiting Circumbinary Planet," *Science* 333 (September 2011): 1602–6, doi:10.1126/science.1210923.

5.   MOA and OGLE Collaborations, "Unbound or Distant Planetary Mass Population Detected by Gravitational Microlensing," *Nature* 473 (May 2011): 349–52, doi:10.1038/nature10092.

6.   Louis E. Strigari et al., "Nomads of the Galaxy," *Monthly Notices of the Royal Astronomical Society* 423 (June 2012): 1856–65, doi:10.1111/j.1365-2966.2012.21009.x.

7.   Norio Narita et al., "First Evidence of a Retrograde Orbit of a Transiting Exoplanet HAT-P-7b," *Publications of the Astronomical Society of Japan* 61 (October 2009): L35–40, doi:10.1093/pasj/61.5.L35; Didier Queloz et al., "*WASP-8b*: A Retrograde Transiting Planet in a Multiple System," *Astronomy and Astrophysics* 517 (July 2010): id. L1, doi:10.1051/0004-6361/201014768; Daniel D. R. Bayliss et al., "Confirmation of a Retrograde Orbit for Exoplanet WASP-17b," *Astrophysical Journal Letters* 722 (October 2010): L224–27, doi:10.1088/2041-8205/722/2/L224.

8.   Rebecca G. Martin and Mario Livio, "On the Formation of Super-Earths with Implications for the Solar System," *Astrophysical Journal* 822 (May 2016): 90, doi:10.3847/0004-637X/822/2/90.

Chapter 3: Can Life Move around in the Universe?

1.   For the most up-to-date distances of the Voyager 1 and Voyager 2 probes, see "Where Are the Voyagers?," NASA, accessed April 25, 2017, http://voyager.jpl.nasa.gov/where.

2.   Donald M. Hassler et al., "Mars' Surface Radiation Environment Measured with the Mars Science Laboratory's Curiosity Rover," *Science* 343 (January 2014): id. 1244797, doi:10.1126/science.1244797.

3.   "High Radiation Doses," US Nuclear Regulatory Commission, last modified October 17, 2014, http://www.nrc.gov/about-nrc/radiation/health-effects/high-rad-doses.html.

4.   University of Colorado Anschutz Medical Campus, "Unpacking Space Radiation to Control Astronaut, Earthbound Cancer Risk," *Science News* (blog), ScienceDaily, March 11, 2016, https://www.sciencedaily.com/releases/2016/03/160311105549.htm.

5.   S. M. Krimigis et al., "Search for the Exit: Voyager 1 at Heliosphere's Border with the Galaxy," *Science* 341 (July 2013): 144–47, doi:10.1126/science.1235721.

6.   Kay D. Bidle et al., "Fossil Genes and Microbes in the Oldest Ice on Earth," *Proceedings of the National Academy of Sciences, USA* 104 (August 2007): 13455–60, doi:10.1073/pnas.0702196104.

7.   Kay D. Bidle et al., "Fossil Genes and Microbes in the Oldest Ice on Earth," *Proceedings of the National Academy of Sciences, USA* 104 (August 2007): 13455–60, doi:10.1073/pnas.0702196104.

Chapter 4: Just How Important Is Liquid Water?

1.   Michael Denton, *Nature's Destiny: How the Laws of Biology Reveal Purpose in the Universe* (New York: Free Press, 1998); Martin Chaplin, "Anomalous Properties of Water," *Water Structure and Science* (blog), last modified October 18, 2016, http://www.lsbu.ac.uk/water/anmlies.html; Ruth M. Lynden-Bell et al., eds., *Water and Life: The Unique Properties of H_2O* (Boca Raton: CRC Press, 2010); Rudolf Podgornik, review of *Water and Life: The Unique Properties of H_2O*, eds. Ruth M. Lynden-Bell et al., *Journal of Biological Physics* 37 (March 2011): 163–65, doi:10.1007/s10867-011-9217-9.

2.   Unless specifically indicated, all discussion of water's properties assumes normal atmospheric pressures and temperatures.

3.   Kenneth Connors, *Chemical Kinetics: The Study of Reaction Rates in Solution* (New York: VCH Publishers, 1990), 14.

4.   C. P. McKay and H. D. Smith, "Possibilities for Methanogenic Life in Liquid Methane on the Surface of Titan," *Icarus* 178 (November 2005): 274–76, doi:10.1016/j.icarus.2005.05.018.

5.   Charles Tanford, "The Hydrophobic Effect and the Organization of Living Matter," *Science* 200 (June 1978): 1012–18, doi:10.1126/science.653353.

6.   Stephen Lower, "States of Matter: Water and Hydrogen Bonding," Chem 1 Virtual Textbook, last modified August 26, 2010, http://www.chem1.com/acad/webtext/states/water.html.

7.   More technically, the one 2s and three 2p orbitals of the oxygen atom hybridize to form four sp³ orbitals. Each of these orbitals need to be filled with two electrons. Oxygen has six outer-shell electrons and each of the two hydrogen atoms has one, giving a total of eight electrons. Thus, the oxygen strongly attracts the hydrogen electrons, and this fills all four of the sp³ orbitals. In order to minimize the electrostatic repulsion among the electrons, they form a tetrahedral structure so that the pairs will be separated from one another with an angle of 109 degrees. However, the positive charge of the hydrogen atoms modifies this arrangement slightly so that the H-O-H bond angle is 104.5 degrees.

8.   The term "hydrogen bonding" does not simply refer to a hydrogen atom

bonding to other elements. It refers to a specific kind of intermolecular bonding. It is not a true chemical bond but rather a special type of electrostatic attraction in which one molecule "donates" a hydrogen to another molecule that "accepts" the hydrogen. The terminology reflects how the slight negative charge of the electrons in one molecule attracts the slight positive charge associated with the hydrogen in another molecule.

9. Before the quantum revolution in the late 1800s and early 1900s, scientists envisioned the world in a classical way. Specifically, time and space were absolute and unchanging. Matter and energy behaved in a continuous fashion such that one could conceivably divide them into arbitrarily small amounts (at least until you reached the last atom) without changing the fundamental properties of the matter or energy. Additionally, one could determine any and all characteristics of the matter and energy to an arbitrary precision. However, according to quantum mechanics, all things (space, time, matter, and energy) come in discrete bundles. Furthermore, fundamental limits exist on how precisely scientists can measure certain quantities (like the position and momentum of a particle) at the same time.

10. Robert A. Kuharski and Peter J. Rossky, "A Quantum Mechanical Study of Structure in Liquid H_2O and D_2O," *Journal of Chemical Physics* 82 (June 1985): 5164–77, doi:10.1063/1.448641.

11. Scott Habershon, Thomas E. Markland, and David E. Manolopoulos, "Competing Quantum Effects in the Dynamics of a Flexible Water Model," *Journal of Chemical Physics* 131 (July 2009): id. 024501, doi:10.1063/1.3167790.

12. Anita Zeidler et al., "Oxygen as a Site Specific Probe of the Structure of Water and Oxide Materials," *Physical Review Letters* 107 (September 2011): id. 145501, doi:10.1103/PhysRevLett.107.145501.

Chapter 5: Why Is Plate Tectonics Essential?

1. Thorne Lay et al., "The Great Sumatra-Andaman Earthquake of 26 December 2004," *Science* 308 (May 2005): 1127–33, doi:10.1126/science.1112250.

2. For a more detailed discussion of how plate tectonics lead to continent building and of the importance of continents for life, see Peter D. Ward and Donald Brownlee, *Rare Earth: Why Complex Life Is Uncommon in the Universe* (New York: Copernicus Books, 2004), 191–220.

3. Derrick Hasterok and David S. Chapman, "Continental Thermal Isostasy: 2. Application to North America," *Journal of Geophysical Research* 112 (June 2007): id. B06415, doi:10.1029/2006JB004664. To view the implications of this modeling for specific cities, see University of Utah, "Without Hot Rock, Much of North America Would Be Underwater," *Science News* (blog), ScienceDaily, June 25, 2007, https://www.sciencedaily.com/releases/2007/06/070625080927.htm.

4. University of Utah, "Without Hot Rock."

5. Normally, water dissolves solids (like salt) by separating it into ions (Na^+ and Cl^-) and surrounding those ions with water molecules. However, in this instance, the water molecule actually separates into a hydrogen ion (H^+) and a hydroxide ion (OH^-) that are dispersed throughout the rock.

6. Katrin Mierdel et al., "Water Solubility in Aluminous Orthopyroxene and the Origin of Earth's Asthenosphere," *Science* 315 (January 2007): 364–68, doi:10.1126/science.1135422.

7. An Yin, "Structural Analysis of the Valles Marineris Fault Zone: Possible Evidence for Large-Scale Strike-Slip Faulting on Mars," *Lithosphere* 4 (August 2012): 286–330, doi:10.1130/L192.1.

8. David Bercovici and Yanick Ricard, "Plate Tectonics, Damage and Inheritance," *Nature* 508 (April 2014): 513–16, doi:10.1038/nature13072.

9. V. S. Solomatov and L.-N. Moresi, "Stagnant Lid Convection on Venus," *Journal of Geophysical Research* 101 (February 1996): 4737–53, doi:10.1029/95JE03361.

10. Richard Ghail, "Rheological and Petrological Implications for a Stagnant Lid Regime on Venus," *Planetary and Space Science* 113–14 (August 2015): 2–9, doi:10.1016/j.pss.2015.02.005.

11. Mierdel, "Water Solubility."

12. James F. Kasting, Daniel P. Whitmire, and Ray T. Reynolds, "Habitable Zones around Main Sequence Stars," *Icarus* 101 (January 1993): 108–28, doi:10.1006/icar.1993.1010.

Chapter 6: Must Life Be Carbon-Based?

1. Dmitry I. Mendeleev, "Über die Beziehungen der Eigenschaften zu den Atomgewichten der Elemente," *Zeitschrift für Chemie* (1869), 405–6. The title translates to "On the Relation of the Properties to the Atomic Weights of the Elements."

2. Scientists classify elements by the number of protons (known as the atomic number Z) they contain. All elements with $Z \leq 94$ are found in

measurable amounts on Earth. Elements with $Z > 94$ no longer exist at measurable levels. A number of the naturally occurring elements, like technetium at $Z = 43$ and plutonium with $Z = 94$, only exist naturally on Earth as decay products from other long-lived radioactive elements.

3.   *CRC Handbook of Chemistry and Physics*, ed. David R. Lide, 84th ed. (Boca Raton, FL: CRC Press, 2003), 4.1, s.v. "The Elements" by C. R. Hammond.

4.   Carl Sagan, *Carl Sagan's Cosmic Connection: An Extraterrestrial Perspective*, (Cambridge: Cambridge University Press, 1973): 46–47.

5.   *CRC Handbook*, 4.1.

6.   For more details, see Fazale Rana, *Creating Life in the Lab* (Grand Rapids: Baker Books, 2011), 137–52.

7.   Norman R. Pace, "The Universal Nature of Biochemistry," *Proceedings of the National Academy of Sciences, USA* 98 (January 2001): 805–8, doi:10.1073/pnas.98.3.805.

8.   William Klemperer, "Astronomical Chemistry," *Annual Review of Physical Chemistry* 62 (May 2011): 173–84, doi:10.1146/annurev-physchem-032210-103332.

9.   Cologne Database for Molecular Spectroscopy ("Molecules in Space," accessed April 25, 2017), http://www.astro.uni-koeln.de/cdms/molecules.

10.   "Frederic Stanley Kipping Award in Silicon Chemistry," American Chemical Society, accessed March 9, 2017, https://www.acs.org/content/acs/en/funding-and-awards/awards/national/bytopic/frederic-stanley-kipping-award-in-silicon-chemistry.html

11.   An "atm" is the amount of pressure exerted by Earth's atmosphere when measured at sea level. One atm is equivalent to 14.7 psi, 760 mm-HG, and 101.3 kPa. Because atmospheric pressure varies with latitude, "atm" was originally designated as the sea level air pressure at the latitude of Paris, France.

12.   William Bains, "Many Chemistries Could Be Used to Build Living Systems," *Astrobiology* 4 (September 2004): 137–67, doi:10.1089/153110704323175124.

13.   National Research Council of the National Academies et al., *The Limits of Organic Life in Planetary Systems* (Washington, DC: National Academies Press, 2007).

14.   Fazale Rana, *The Cell's Design* (Grand Rapids: Baker Books, 2008), 35–52.

15.   Sagan, *Carl Sagan's Cosmic Connection*, 46–47.

Chapter 7: What Does "Habitable" Mean?

1. Harlow Shapley, ed., *Climatic Change: Evidence, Causes, and Effects* (Cambridge: Harvard University Press, 1953), 318.

2. Elisa V. Quintana et al., "An Earth-Sized Planet in the Habitable Zone of a Cool Star," *Science* 344 (April 2014): 277–80, doi:10.1126/science.1249403; Gemini Observatory, "First Potentially Habitable Earth-Sized Planet Confirmed by Gemini and Keck Observatories," *Science News* (blog), ScienceDaily, April 17, 2014, https://www.sciencedaily.com/releases/2014/04/140417141946.htm.

3. Jon M. Jenkins et al., "Discovery and Validation of Kepler-452b: A 1.6 R Super Earth Exoplanet in the Habitable Zone of a G2 Star," *Astronomical Journal* 150 (August 2015): 56, doi:10.1088/0004-6256/150/2/56.

4. Erik A. Petigura, Andrew W. Howard, and Geoffrey W. Marcy, "Prevalence of Earth-Size Planets Orbiting Sun-like Stars," *Proceedings of the National Academy of Sciences, USA* 110 (November 2013): 19273–78, doi:10.1073/pnas.1319909110.

5. David R. Williams, "Planetary Fact Sheet—Metric," NASA, last modified December 9, 2016, http://nssdc.gsfc.nasa.gov/planetary/factsheet.

6. M. Podolak, A. Weizman, and M. Marley, "Comparative Models of Uranus and Neptune," *Planetary and Space Science* 43 (December 1995): 1517–22, doi:10.1016/0032-0633(95)00061-5.

7. Leslie A. Rogers, "*Most* 1.6 Earth-Radius Planets Are Not Rocky," *Astrophysical Journal* 801 (March 2015): 41, doi:10.1088/0004-637X/801/1/41; Eric D. Lopez and Jonathan J. Fortney, "Understanding the Mass-Radius Relation for Sub-Neptunes: Radius as a Proxy for Composition," *Astrophysical Journal* 792 (September 2014): 1, doi:10.1088/0004-637X/792/1/1.

8. As photons from the star impact the molecules in the atmosphere of an exoplanet, the molecules increase in velocity. If the radiation imparts enough energy to the molecules, they acquire sufficient speeds to escape the gravitational pull of the planet, thus evaporating into space.

9. James E. Owen and Subhanjoy Mohanty, "Habitability of Terrestrial-Mass Planets in the HZ of M Dwarfs—I. H/He-Dominated Atmospheres," *Monthly Notices of the Royal Astronomical Society* 459 (July 2016): 4088–108, doi:10.1093/mnras/stw959.

10. Vladimir S. Airapetian et al., "How Hospitable Are Space Weather Affected Habitable Zones? The Role of Ion Escape," *Astrophysical Journal Letters* 836 (February 2017): L3, doi:10.3847/2041-8213/836/1/L3.

11. William C. Danchi and Bruno Lopez, "Effect of Metallicity on the Evolution of the Habitable Zone from the Pre-Main Sequence to the Asymptotic Giant Branch and the Search for Life," *Astrophysical Journal* 769 (May 2013): 27, doi:10.1088/0004-637X/769/1/27.

12. Nola Taylor Redd, "The Odds for Life on a Moonless Earth," *Astrobiology Magazine*, August 4, 2011, http://www.astrobio.net/news-exclusive/the-odds-for-life-on-a-moonless-earth; Keith Cooper, "Earth's Moon May Not Be Critical to Life," *Astrobiology Magazine*, January 26, 2015, http://www.astrobio.net/news-exclusive/earths-moon-may-not-critical-life.

13. Jeff Zweerink, "GOE or Die: Earth's Habitability No Sure Thing," *Today's New Reason to Believe* (blog), Reasons to Believe, September 1, 2009, http://www.reasons.org/articles/goe-or-die-earth's-habitability-no-sure-thing.

14. Jeff Zweerink, "Oxygen Spikes Jumpstart Life's Complexity and Size," *Today's New Reason to Believe* (blog), Reasons to Believe, March 1, 2010, http://www.reasons.org/articles/oxygen-spikes-jumpstart-life-s-complexity-and-size.

15. Jeff Zweerink, "A Hazy Atmosphere on Early Earth," *Today's New Reason to Believe* (blog), Reasons to Believe, April 16, 2012, http://www.reasons.org/articles/a-hazy-atmosphere-on-early-earth.

Chapter 8: How Would We Know If Life Exists Out There?

1.   Michael J. Mumma et al., "Strong Release of Methane on Mars in Northern Summer 2003," *Science* 323 (February 2009): 1041–45, doi:10.1126/science.1165243; and Christopher R. Webster et al., "Mars Methane Detection and Variability at Gale Crater," *Science* 347 (January 2015): 415–17, doi:10.1126/science.1261713.

2.   One of many inorganic processes that could produce the quantities of methane seen on Mars is described in Christopher Oze and Mukul Sharma, "Have Olivine, Will Gas: Serpentinization and the Abiogenic Production of Methane on Mars," *Geophysical Research Letters* 32 (May 2005): L10203, doi:10.1029/2005GL022691.

3.   Specifically, the shift in wavelength tells astronomers the speed of the object along the line of sight. Shifts to shorter wavelengths result from motion toward Earth, where shifts to longer wavelengths arise from motion away from Earth.

4.   R. Paul Butler and Geoffrey W. Marcy, "A Planet Orbiting 47 Ursa Majoris," *Astrophysical Journal Letters* 464 (June 1996): L153–56,

doi:10.1086/310102.

5.   Geoffrey W. Marcy and R. Paul Butler, "A Planetary Companion to 70 Virginis," *Astrophysical Journal Letters* 464 (June 1996): L147–51, doi:10.1086/310096.

6.   David Charbonneau et al., "Detection of Planetary Transits across a Sun-like Star," *Astrophysical Journal Letters* 529 (January 2000): L45–48, doi:10.1086/312457.

7.   Gregory W. Henry et al., "A Transiting '51 Peg-like' Planet," *Astrophysical Journal Letters* 529 (January 2000): L41–44, doi:10.1086/312458; David Charbonneau et al., "Detection of Planetary Transits."

8.   I. A. Bond et al., "OGLE 2003-BLG-235/MOA 2003-BLG-53: A Planetary Microlensing Event," *Astrophysical Journal Letters* 606 (May 2004): L155–58, doi:10.1086/420928.

9.   S. Charpinet et al., "A Compact System of Small Planets around a Former Red-Giant Star," *Nature* 480 (December 2011): 496–99, doi:10.1038/nature10631.

10. For an overview, see Joshua Rodriguez, "Flower Power: NASA Reveals Spring Starshade Animation," *Exoplanet Exploration*, NASA, accessed April 25, 2017, https://exoplanets.nasa.gov/resources/1015.

11. S. Seager, W. Bains, and J. J. Petkowski, "Toward a List of Molecules as Potential Biosignature Gases for the Search for Life on Exoplanets and Applications to Terrestrial Biochemistry," *Astrobiology* 16 (June 2016): 465–85, doi:10.1089/ast.2015.1404.

Chapter 9: Does a Multiverse Exist?

1.   This chapter gives a brief outline of many concepts that are developed more fully in my book *Who's Afraid of the Multiverse?* (Pasadena, CA: Reasons to Believe, 2008).

2.   Electrons and protons can combine at nearly any temperature, but at higher temperatures, the collisions and radiation of the particles will separate them at the same rate. Below about 3000°C, the formation rate of neutral hydrogen greatly outpaces the rate of destruction.

3.   A flat universe is important for life because an open universe would expand too rapidly for the stars, galaxies, and clusters of galaxies to form. A closed universe expands too slowly, and most of the mass ends up in black holes.

4.   The picture changes somewhat with the discovery of dark energy and the inclusion of dark matter. However, the fundamental issue of a habit-

able universe depending on incredibly fine-tuned numbers remains.

5.   Thanks to Phil Halper for a nice YouTube video describing the historical progression of ideas and discoveries leading to our current understanding of inflationary big bang cosmology. See "Before the Big Bang 4: Eternal Inflation & The Multiverse," YouTube video, 59:53, posted by "skydivephil," June 28, 2016, https://www.youtube.com/watch?v=QqjsZEZMR7I.

6.   For more details, see Alan Guth, *The Inflationary Universe* (Cambridge: Persues Books, 1997).

Chapter 10: Does a Multiverse Solve All These Problems?

1.   Jeff Zweerink, "The Higgs Boson: Discovered or Nonexistent?," *Today's New Reason to Believe* (blog), Reasons to Believe, July 2, 2012, http://www.reasons.org/articles/the-higgs-boson-discovered-or-nonexistent.

2.   Kimberly Boddy and Sean Carroll, "Can the Higgs Boson Save Us from the Menace of the Boltzmann Brains?," preprint, submitted August 21, 2013, https://arxiv.org/abs/1308.4686.

3.   Andrea De Simone et al., "Boltzmann Brains and the Scale-Factor Cutoff Measure of the Multiverse," *Physical Review D* 82 (September 2010): id. 063520, doi:10.1103/PhysRevD.82.063520.

4.   Raphael Bousso and Claire Zukowski, "Multivacuum Initial Conditions and the Arrow of Time," *Physical Review D* 87 (May 2013): id. 103504, doi:10.1103/PhysRevD.87.103504.

5.   Jeff Zweerink, "'Built-In' Causality Allows Universe's Habitability," *Today's New Reason to Believe* (blog), Reasons to Believe, April 1, 2009, http://www.reasons.org/articles/built-in-causality-allows-universes-habitability.

6.   Sean Carroll, "Boltzmann's Universe," *Preposterous Universe* (blog), January 14, 2008, http://www.preposterousuniverse.com/blog/2008/01/14/boltzmanns-universe.

Chapter 11: Why Isn't Pluto a Planet?

1.   M. E. Brown, C. A. Trujillo, and D. L. Rabinowitz, "Discovery of a Planetary-Sized Object in the Scattered Kuiper Belt," *Astrophysical Journal Letters* 635 (November 2005): L79–100, doi:10.1086/499336.

2.   "Pluto and the Developing Landscape of Our Solar System," International Astronomical Union, accessed April 25, 2017, https://www.iau.org/public/themes/pluto.

3.   Harvard-Smithsonian Center for Astrophysics, "Is Pluto a Planet? The Votes Are In," news release, September 22, 2014, https://www.cfa.harvard.edu/news/2014-25.

4.   Some scientists speculate that moons of planets (both in our solar system and outside it) might meet the conditions for life. We do find evidence of liquid oceans under the ice covering Europa and Enceladus, but it's not clear that those conditions would permit life. And detecting evidence of life on a moon is much more challenging than finding it on an exoplanet.

5.   Pascal Rosenblatt et al., "Accretion of Phobos and Deimos in an Extended Debris Disc Stirred by Transient Moons," Nature Geoscience 9 (August 2016): 581–83, doi:10.1038/ngeo2742.

6.   George Musser, "A Reason for a Moonless Venus," Scientific American 295 (December 1, 2006): 40, doi:10.1038/scientificamerican1206-40a.

Chapter 12: How Long Will Life Last?

1.   Ken Caldeira and James F. Kasting, "The Life Span of the Biosphere Revisited," Nature 360 (December 1992): 721–23, doi:10.1038/360721a0.

2.   Jack T. O'Malley-James et al., "Swansong Biospheres II: The Final Signs of Life on Terrestrial Planets near the End of Their Habitable Lifetimes," International Journal of Astrobiology 13 (July 2014): 229–43, doi:10.1017/S1473550413000426.

3.   Jason C. Sanford, John W. Snedden, and Sean P. S. Gulick, "The Cretaceous-Paleogene Boundary Deposit in the Gulf of Mexico: Large-Scale Oceanic Basin Response to the Chicxulub Impact," Journal of Geophysical Research 121 (March 2016): 1240–61, doi:10.1002/2015JB012615; H. J. Melosh et al., "Ignition of Global Wildfires at the Cretaceous/Tertiary Boundary," Nature 343 (January 18, 1990): 251–54, doi:10.1038/343251a0.

4.   Peter Schulte et al., "The Chicxulub Asteroid Impact and Mass Extinction at the Cretaceous-Paleogene Boundary," Science 327 (March 2010): 1214–18, doi:10.1126/science.1177265.

5.   Ray W. Klebesadel, Ian B. Strong, and Roy A. Olson, "Observations of Gamma-Ray Bursts of Cosmic Origin," Astrophysical Journal 182 (June 1973): L85, doi:10.1086/181225.

6.   A. L. Melott et al., "Did a Gamma-Ray Burst Initiate the Late Ordovician Mass Extinction?," International Journal of Astrobiology 3 (January 2004): 55–61, doi:10.1017/S1473550404001910.

7.   Ibid.
8.   Lawrence M. Krauss and Glenn D. Starkman, "Life, the Universe, and Nothing: Life and Death in an Ever-Expanding Universe," *Astrophysical Journal* 531 (March 2000): 22–30, doi:10.1086/308434.
9.   S. Alekhin, A. Djouadi, and S. Moch, "The Top Quark and Higgs Boson Masses and the Stability of the Electroweak Vacuum," *Physics Letters B* 716 (September 2012): 214–19, doi:10.1016/j.physletb.2012.08.024.
10.   Michael S. Turner and Frank Wilczek, "Is Our Vacuum Metastable?," *Nature* 298 (August 1982): 633–34, doi:10.1038/298633a0.

Chapter 13: Is *Star Wars* Realistic?

1.   Veselin B. Kostov et al., "Kepler-1647b: The Largest and Longest-Period *Kepler* Transiting Circumbinary Planet," *Astrophysical Journal* 827 (August 2016): 86, doi:10.3847/0004-637X/827/1/86.
2.   Charles J. Lada, "Stellar Multiplicity and the Initial Mass Function: Most Stars Are Single," *Astrophysical Journal Letters* 640 (March 2006): L63–66, doi:10.1086/503158.
3.   Elisa V. Quintana and Jack J. Lissauer, "Terrestrial Planet Formation in Binary Star Systems," chap. 10 in *Planets in Binary Star Systems*, ed. Nader Haghighipour (Dordrecht: Springer Netherlands, 2010), 265–83.
4.   Nathan A. Kaib, Sean N. Raymond, and Martin Duncan, "Planetary System Disruption by Galactic Perturbations to Wide Binary Stars," *Nature* 493 (January 2013): 381–84, doi:10.1038/nature11780.
5.   Konstantin Batygin, "A Primordial Origin for Misalignments between Stellar Spin Axes and Planetary Orbits," *Nature* 491 (November 2012): 418–20, doi:10.1038/nature11560.
6.   Elliott P. Horch et al., "Most Sub-Arcsecond Companions of *Kepler* Exoplanet Candidate Host Stars Are Gravitationally Bound," *Astrophysical Journal* 795 (November 2014): 60, doi:10.1088/0004-637X/795/1/60.

Chapter 14: Is Global Warming Bad?

1.   Myles McLeod, "Methane-Making Microbes Appeared Early on Earth," *Daily News* (blog), *New Scientist*, March 22, 2006, https://www.newscientist.com/article/dn8882-methane-making-microbes-appeared-early-on-earth.
2.   Nick M. W. Roberts et al., "Continent Formation through Time," *Geological Society, London, Special Publications* 389 (2015): 1–16, doi:10.1144/SP389.13.

3.   D. G. Pearson, S. W. Parman, and G. M. Nowell, "A Link between Large Mantle Melting Events and Continent Growth Seen in Osmium Isotopes," *Nature* 449 (September 2007): 202–5, doi:10.1038/nature06122.

Chapter 15: Isn't It Arrogant to Think We Are the Only Life?

1.   See "'A Universe from Nothing' by Lawrence Krauss, AAI 2009," YouTube video, 1:04:51, posted by "Richard Dawkins Foundation for Reason & Science," October 21, 2009, https://www.youtube.com/watch?v=7ImvlS8PLIo#t=16m49s.
2.   Dennis R. Danielson, "The Great Copernican Cliché," *American Journal of Physics* 69 (October 2001): 1029–35, doi:10.1119/1.1379734.
3.   Helium and neon rank as the second and fifth most abundant elements. However, neither reacts chemically with other elements, so they play no real role in the functioning of life.
4.   John D. Barrow and Frank J. Tipler, *The Anthropic Cosmological Principle* (Oxford: Oxford University Press, 1986), 253.
5.   Jeff Zweerink, "Universe Designed to Produce Carbon and Oxygen," *Today's New Reason to Believe* (blog), Reasons to Believe, April 8, 2013, http://www.reasons.org/articles/universe-designed-to-produce-carbon-and-oxygen.
6.   Max Tegmark, "Is 'the Theory of Everything' Merely the Ultimate Ensemble Theory?," *Annals of Physics* 270 (November 1998): 1–51, doi:10.1006/aphy.1998.5855.
7.   Fred Hoyle, "The Universe: Past and Present Reflections," *Engineering and Science* (November 1981): 8–12.

Chapter 16: What Does the Bible Say about Life Out There?

1.   Paul Davies, "E.T. and God," *The Atlantic*, September 2003, http://www.theatlantic.com/magazine/archive/2003/09/et-and-god/376856.
2.   Gary Bates, "Did God Create Life on Other Planets?," *Creation*, March 2007, http://creation.com/did-god-create-life-on-other-planets.
3.   Kenneth Samples, "Imago Dei: What Does It Mean?," *Today's New Reason to Believe* (blog), Reasons to Believe, August 1, 2011, http://www.reasons.org/articles/imago-dei-what-does-it-mean.
4.   Since Copernicus, there has been an abundance of evidence to demonstrate that Earth obviously orbits around the Sun. But the idea that this represents a demotion seems like a twentieth century reinterpretation of history. For a historical look at how Copernicus's work affected our

understanding of our place in the universe, see Dennis R. Danielson, "The Great Copernican Cliché," *American Journal of Physics* 69 (October 2001): 1029–35, doi:10.1119/1.1379734.

5. For a concise look at the essentials of eschatology, see Kenneth Samples, *Christian Endgame* (Covina, CA: RTB Press, 2013).

6. Mark Van Bebber, "What Does the Bible Say about Intelligent Life on Other Planets?," Christian Answers Network, accessed April 25, 2017, http://christiananswers.net/q-eden/edn-c012.html.

Chapter 17: What Kinds of Life Are Possible?

1. Just to be clear, the latter situation (royal flush with an ace of the wrong suit) occurs three times more often than the royal flush with the proper ace—at least if the number of hands is large enough but finite.

2. Andrea De Simone et al., "Boltzmann Brains and the Scale-Factor Cutoff Measure of the Multiverse," *Physical Review D* 82 (September 2010): id. 063520, doi:10.1103/PhysRevD.82.063520.

3. See Paul Davies, *The Cosmic Jackpot* (Boston: Houghton Mifflin, 2007), 179–90.

Chapter 18: Why Did God Wait So Long to Create Humans?

1. "A Pale Blue Dot," The Planetary Society, accessed April 25, 2017, http://www.planetary.org/explore/space-topics/earth/pale-blue-dot.html.

2. Terry Mortenson, "The Fall and the Problem of Millions of Years of Natural Evil," *Answers in Depth*, July 18, 2012, https://answersingenesis.org/theory-of-evolution/millions-of-years/the-fall-and-the-problem-of-millions-of-years-of-natural-evil.

3. The radiation emitted as lighter elements fuse into heavier ones provides a pressure that supports the outer layers of the star. When the fuel for fusion is exhausted, the outer layers collapse toward the center of the star.

4. C. Scott et al., "Tracing the Stepwise Oxygenation of the Proterozoic Ocean," *Nature* 452 (March 2008): 456–59, doi:10.1038/nature06811.

5. Kathleen A. McFadden et al., "Pulsed Oxidation and Biological Evolution in the Ediacaran Doushantuo Formation," *Proceedings of the National Academy of Sciences, USA* 105 (March 2008): 3197–202, doi:10.1073/pnas.0708336105.

6. Peter E. Driscoll, "Simulating 2 Ga of Geodynamo History," *Geophysical Research Letters* 43 (June 2016): 5680–87, doi:10.1002/2016GL068858.

Chapter 19: Would the Discovery of ET Disprove Christianity?

1. *Praying Together*, English Language Liturgical Consultation (1988).
2. See Fazale Rana and Hugh Ross, *Origins of Life: Biblical and Evolutionary Models Face Off* (Covina, CA: RTB Press, 2014); and Hugh Ross, *Improbable Planet: How Earth Became Humanity's Home* (Grand Rapids: Baker Books, 2016).
3. For a starting point into the theological significance of finding intelligent ET, see Ted Peters, "The Implications of the Discovery of Extra-Terrestrial Life for Religion," *Philosophical Transactions of the Royal Society A* 369 (February 2011): 644–55, doi:10.1098/rsta.2010.0234.
4. For one quick example, see "Interpretations of Quantum Mechanics," *Wikipedia*, last modified April 25, 2017, https://en.wikipedia.org/wiki/Interpretations_of_quantum_mechanics. I realize that *Wikipedia* may have some scholarly deficiencies, but this page lists at least 13 different interpretations of quantum mechanics and provides links to investigate those interpretations more thoroughly.

Chapter 20: Must ET Exist?

1. David Sobral et al., "A Large Hα Survey at z = 2.23, 1.47, 0.84 and 0.40: The 11 Gyr Evolution of Star-Forming Galaxies from HiZELS," *Monthly Notices of the Royal Astronomical Society* 428 (January 2013): 1128–46, doi:10.1093/mnras/sts096.
2. *Contact*, directed by Robert Zemeckis (Burbank, CA: Warner Home Video, 1997), DVD.
3. Fazale Rana and Hugh Ross, *Origins of Life: Biblical and Evolutionary Models Face Off* (Covina, CA: RTB Press, 2014), 75–79.
4. J. Alexis P. Rodriguez et al., "Tsunami Waves Extensively Resurfaced the Shorelines of an Early Martian Ocean," *Scientific Reports* 6 (2016): id. 25106, doi:10.1038/srep25106.
5. W. T. Pike et al., "Quantification of the Dry History of the Martian Soil Inferred from In Situ Microscopy," *Geophysical Research Letters* 38 (December 2011): id. L24201, doi:10.1029/2011GL049896.
6. Amos Banin, "The Enigma of the Martian Soil," *Science* 309 (August 2005): 888–90, doi:10.1126/science.1112794; Donald M. Hassler et al., "Mars' Surface Radiation Environment Measured with the Mars Science Laboratory's Curiosity Rover," *Science* 343 (January 2014): id. 1244797, doi:10.1126/science.1244797.
7. Finding life on other planets/moons in the solar system would not mean

that life originated there. Past research shows that impacts and the solar wind move life from Earth to other bodies. Even if scientists found life somewhere else in the solar system, we would need to address whether it arose there or if it was transported from Earth.

8.   *Contact*, directed by Robert Zemeckis (Burbank, CA: Warner Home Video, 1997), DVD.

Index

About the Author

 Astrophysicist **Jeff Zweerink** is a research scholar and executive director of online learning at Reasons to Believe (RTB), an organization dedicated to demonstrating the compatibility of science and Christianity. He earned a PhD in astrophysics with a focus on gamma rays from Iowa State University. Jeff was involved in research projects such as STACEE and VERITAS and is a coauthor on more than 30 academic papers. He is also the author of *Who's Afraid of the Multiverse?* and coauthor of the *Impact Events* student devotionals. Today, Jeff oversees RTB's accredited online learning programs and works on GAPS, a balloon experiment seeking to detect dark matter.

Jeff and his wife, Lisa, live in Southern California with their five children.

About Reasons to Believe

Uniquely positioned within the science-faith discussion since 1986, Reasons to Believe (RTB) communicates that science and faith are, and always will be, allies, not enemies. Distinguished for integrating science and faith respectfully and with integrity, RTB welcomes dialogue with both skeptics and believers. Addressing topics such as the origin of the universe, the origin and history of life, and the origin, history, and destiny of humanity, RTB's website offers a vast array of helpful resources. Through their books, blogs, podcasts, and speaking events, RTB scholars present powerful reasons from science to trust in the reliability of the Bible and the message it conveys about creation and redemption.

For more information, contact us via:
www.reasons.org
818 S. Oak Park Rd.
Covina, CA 91724
(855) REASONS | (855) 732-7667

In *Who's Afraid of the Multiverse?* Dr. Jeff Zweerink demonstrates once again that we should not be afraid of new scientific discoveries. As the multiverse theory becomes increasingly popular, Christians can see this as an opportunity to address skeptics' concerns with gentleness, respect, and confidence.

www.reasons.org

RTB_OFFICIAL

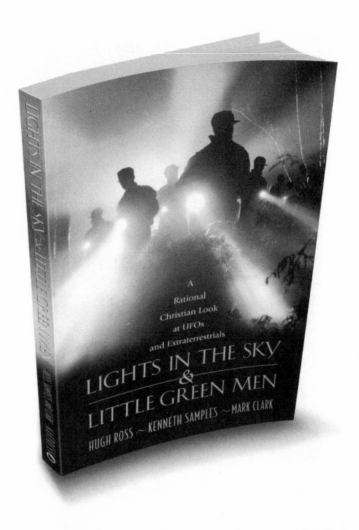

Does documentation exist for UFO sightings and landings?
Is there a relationship between UFO sightings and demonology?
Working from a rational Christian worldview, *Lights in the Sky and Little Green Men* initiates a search for truth to answers about extraterrestrial life, cult groups, alien encounters, and more.

www.reasons.org

RTB_OFFICIAL